Ring A Ring O'Roses

Fingerplays for Preschool Children

⊱⋅⊰⊶⊙⊷⊱⋅⊰

11th Edition
⊱⋅⊰⊶⊙⊷⊱⋅⊰

Flint Public Library

Flint, Michigan

Ring A Ring O'Roses
Eleventh Edition

ISBN 0-9654589-1-1

4959

Order from
Flint Public Library
Business Office
1026 East Kearsley
Flint, Michigan 48502-1994
(810) 232-7111

This publication serves as a practical handbook for the storytellers in the Flint Public Library's Preschool Storyhour program. Through the years it has become an essential resource for teachers, librarians and daycare providers the world over.

Every effort has been made to ascertain proper ownership of copyrighted materials and obtain permission for their use. Any omission is unintentional and will be corrected in future printings upon proper notification.

Compilers and Editors:

1955 Virginia Totten
1958 Virginia Totten
1961 Ruth Maurer
1966 Gertrude Keyworth
1971 Gertrude Keyworth
1975 Gertrude Keyworth
1977 Gertrude Keyworth
1981 Gertrude Keyworth
1988 Cynthia Stilley
1996 Charles Hansen and Cynthia Stilley
2000 Charles Hansen and Cynthia Stilley

Cover design: Kris Indianer

Thanks to Armando Trejo of the Gail Borden Public Library District in Elgin, Illinois, for help on the Spanish translations.

To All Our Preschoolers

Come join our parade. We'll have lots of fun,
As we march through the pages, one by one.

You don't need a horn or a drum that will beat.
All you will need are your hands and your feet.

Your feet tap the rhythm. Your hands will keep time,
As you act out your favorite fingerplay rhyme.

Todd plays he's a train chugging 'round the track.
Please climb aboard. "Toot! Toot!" Now you're back.

Kris likes the animals in the woods and the zoo.
He can hop like a bunny, and so can you.

Would you care to join Katie for a cup of tea?
Or maybe it's a rag doll you'd rather be.

Whatever it is you care to pretend,
You can choose as we march from beginning to end.

—Gertrude Keyworth—

Subjects

In addition to the following Subject Index, be sure to check the alphabetically listed fingerplays for titles that begin with the subject you are searching. For instance, "Baby Seeds" is about seeds and is therefore listed in this Subject Index under "Seeds." But you will also find it included with other fingerplays that have "Baby" ("Baby Bumblebee," "Baby Kangaroo," etc.) as the first word of their titles.

A

Abranlas, Ciérrenlas
(Open, Shut Them)

Abranlas, ciérrenlas,
(Open, shut them.)
> *Open, close hands.*

Abranlas, ciérrenlas,
(Open, shut them.)
> *Open, close hands.*

Pla, pla, pla, pla, pla.
(Give a little clap,)
> *Clap, clap...*

Abranlas, ciérrenlas,
(Open, shut them.)
> *Open, close hands.*

Abranlas, ciérrenlas,
(Open, shut them.)
> *Open, close hands.*

Póngalas acá.
(Put them in your lap.)
> *Fold hands in lap.*

After a Bath

After my bath, I try, try, try

To wipe myself 'till I'm dry, dry, dry.

Hands to wipe, and fingers and toes,

And two wet legs and a shiny nose.

Just think how much less time I'd take,

If I were a dog, and could shake, shake, shake.
> *Suit action to words.*

The Airplane

The airplane has great big wings;
> *Arms outstretched.*

Its propeller spins around and sings
> *Make one arm go around.*

"Vvvvvvv!"

The airplane goes up;
> *Lift arms.*

The airplane goes down;
> *Lower arms.*

The airplane flies high
> *Arms outstretched, turn body around.*

Over our town!

All for Baby

Here's a ball for baby,
Touch fingertips, forming ball.

Big and soft and round.

Here is baby's hammer,
Pound one fist on other.

Oh, how he can pound.

Here is baby's music
Clap hands.

Clapping, clapping so.

Here are baby's soldiers
Hold ten fingers erect.

Standing in a row.

Here is baby's trumpet
One fist in front of other at mouth.

Toot, too, too, too, too.

Here's the way that baby

Plays at peek-a-boo.
Spread fingers in front of eyes.

Here's a big umbrella
Hold index finger of right hand erect.
Place palm of left hand on top of finger.

To keep the baby dry.

Here is baby's cradle,
Make cradle of interlocked fingers,
knuckles up, erect index and smallest
fingers.

Rock-a-baby bye.
Rock hands.

All by Myself

There are many things that I can do,
   All by myself;
I can comb my hair and lace my shoe,
   All by myself;
I can wash my hands and my face,
   All by myself;
I can put my toys and blocks in place,
   All by myself.

Suit actions to words.

Animals

Can you hop like a rabbit?
Can you jump like a frog?
Can you walk like a duck?
Can you run like a dog?
Can you fly like a bird?
Can you swim like a fish?
And be still like a good child,
As still as this?

Suit actions to words.

Ant Hill

Once I saw an ant hill
Fingers curled under, concealed.

With no ants about.

So I said, "Dear little ants,

Won't you come out?"

Then, as if the little ants

Had heard my call,

One, two, three, four, five came out!
*As numbers are called, fingers are
extended.*

And that was all.

Aplaudir con las Manos
(Clap Your Hands)

Con esta mano derecha,
(With this right hand,)
Raise right hand.

Y esta mano izquierda,
(And with this left hand,)
Raise left hand.

Se juntan las palmas para aplaudir.
(I put them together to clap.)
Put palms together.

Rudioso, quedo, quedito.
(Loud, quiet, quiet.)
Clap loudly.

Apple Tree

Away up high in the apple tree,
Hold hands above head.

Two red apples smiled at me.
*Form circles with thumb and forefinger
of each hand. Smile.*

I shook that tree as hard as I could.
Put hands out as if on tree — shake.

And down came the apples,
Hands above head and lower to ground.

Mmmmmm were they good.
Rub tummy.

April First

Little bears have three feet.
Hold up three fingers.

Little bears have four.
Use four fingers in same way.

Little cows have two feet.
Use two fingers in same way.

And girls and boys have more.
Use five fingers in same way.

Do you believe my story?
Point to "you", point to own temple.

I'll tell it only once a year.
Hold up index finger for "once."

When April comes along.
Clap hands to express pleasure.

APRIL FOOL!

April Trickery

The big round sun
> *Form a circle with fingers of both hands.*

In an April sky,
> *Raise arms to form circle over head.*

Winked at a cloud

That was passing by.

The gray cloud laughed

As it scattered rain.
> *Pretend to scatter rain with fingers.*

Then out came the big,

Round sun again.
> *Form circle with fingers of both hands.*

Around and About

Around and about,

Around and about,
> *Circular motion of index finger.*

Over and under
> *Swooping over and under motions.*

And in and out.
> *In and out motions with hand.*

Run through the meadow,
> *Running motion — hands and arms.*

Swim in the sea,
> *Swimming motion — hands and arms.*

Slide down a mountain,
> *Sliding motions with hands.*

Climb up a tree!
> *Climbing motions with hands.*

La Araña
(The Spider)

La araña pirulina
(The little spider)

Por la pared se subió
(Climbed up the wall)
> *Walk right fingers up left arm.*

Y mi Tía Catalina
(And my Aunt Katharine)

Con la escoba la barrió. barrído
(Swept him away with a broom.)
> *Clap hands together.*

Auto, Auto

Auto, auto may I have a ride?
> *Make fists, thumbs up. One thumb moves as if talking to other.*

Yes sir; yes, sir; step right inside.
> *One thumb talks.*

Pour in the water
> *Move first thumb as if pouring water.*

Turn on the gas.
> *Move same thumb and index finger to turn switch.*

Chug-away, chug-away,
> *Pretend to hold steering wheel.*

But do not go too fast.

Autumn

Leaves are floating softly down.
> *Use arms in up and down motions.*

They make a carpet on the ground.

Then swish, the wind comes whistling
   by,
> *Move arms from one side to the other.*

And sends them dancing to the sky.
> *Let hands flutter up into the air.*

B

Baby Bumble Bee

(Tune of "Turkey In the Straw.")

I'm bringing home a baby bumble bee.
*One hand cupped over the other,
pretending to carry a bee.*

Won't my mama be so proud of me.

I'm bringing home a baby bumble bee.

Ouch! — h-h-he stung me.

I'm squashing up my baby bumble
bee.
Squash palms together.

Won't my mama be so proud of me.

I'm squashing up my baby bumble
bee.

O - o - o - o it's all over me.

I'm wiping off my baby bumble bee.
Wipe hands on clothes.

Won't my mama be so proud of me.

I'm wiping off my baby bumble bee.

Now my mama won't spank-k-k me!

Baby Kangaroo

Jump, jump, jump
*Make jumping motion with index
finger of right hand.*

Goes the big kangaroo.

I thought there was one,

But I see there are two.

The mother takes her young one

Along in a pouch,
*Index finger of left hand slips into fist of
right hand.*

Where he can nap like a child

On a couch.

Jump, jump, jump.
*Continue making jumping motion
while left index finger is in right fist.*

Jump, jump, jump.

Baby Seeds

In a milkweed cradle
Form cradle with both hands.

Snug and warm,

Baby seeds are hiding

Safe from harm.

Open wide the cradle
Open hands.

Hold it high.
Hands up high.

Come, Mr. Wind,

Help them fly.
Wave arm above head.

Baby's Bath

Baby's ready for his bath.

Here's the baby's tub.
Make circle with arms.

Here's the baby's washcloth.
Hold hand up, palm flat.

See how he can rub.
Pretend to rub face.

Here's the baby's cake of soap,
Make a fist.

And here's the towel dry,
Hold hands flat, thumbs touching.

And here's the baby's cradle

Rock-a-baby-bye.
Make imaginary cradle and rock it back and forth.

Baby's House

Sally O'Neil learned this from her grand-mother, Laura Wood, who was born in 1886 in Tennessee.

Ring the bell,
Pull baby's ear.

Knock on the door,
Knock on his forehead.

Peep in the window,
Pull under eyelid.

Open the latch,
Open mouth.

Walk right in.
Walk fingers into mouth.

Chin chopper,

Chin chopper,

Chin.
Chuck under the chin.

Baby's Nap

This is a baby ready for a nap.
Hold up finger.

Lay him down in his mother's lap.
Place in palm of hand.

Cover him up so he won't peep.
Wrap other fingers to cover him.

Rock him 'till he's fast asleep.
Rock hands to and fro.

The Bakery

Down around the corner
Point hand to the right.

In the bakery shop

There were ten little doughnuts,
Hold up ten fingers.

With sugar on top.

Along came Katie all alone,

She grabbed a big one and ran on
home.
Clap hands together once.

The Ball

Here's a ball I keep on the shelf.
Form circle with fingers. Place on shelf.

I can toss it, and catch it,

And bounce it myself.
Pretend to toss, catch and bounce.

Here is a ball, I'll toss it to you.

Please catch it and toss it

Right back to me, too.
Use appropriate motions.

Balloons

This is the way we blow our balloons.
*Round hands as if holding a balloon,
spreading farther and farther apart. Or
make a circle, with children holding
hands. Enlarge the circle, bigger and
bigger.*

Blow, blow, blow.

This is the way we break our balloons,
Oh! Oh! Oh!
*Clap hands together on each "Oh!" Or
drop hands in circle and fall down.*

Beehive

Here is the little beehive.
*Hold up hand with fingers curled
under.*

Where are the bees?

Hidden away where nobody sees.

Soon they come creeping out of the
hive.

One, two, three, four, five.
Raise thumb and fingers, one at a time.

Bend and Stretch

Bend and stretch, reach for the stars.
There goes Jupiter, here comes Mars.

Bend and stretch, reach for the sky.
Stand on tip-e-toe, oh! so high!

Suit actions to words.

Big Hill

Here's a great big hill
Extend arm sideways to form hill.

With snow all over the side.

Let's take our sleds
Place hand on extended shoulder.

And down the hill we'll slide.
Slide hand down arm.

A Big Old Frog

by Chuck Schacht, Romeo, MI

A big old frog with a long pink tongue
> *Put one fist on top of other hand. Wiggle index finger as a tongue.*

Lived in our garden when I was
young.
He ate caterpillars and beetles too,
> *Snap "frog" hand as if snapping at insects.*

And if you picked him up,
He'd mess on you.
> *You choose this one!!!*

A Birthday

Today is _____'s birthday.
> *Insert name of child.*

Let's make her (him) a cake.
> *Form cake with hands.*

Mix and stir,
> *Action of stirring.*

Stir and mix,

Then into the oven to bake.
> *Pretend to place cake in oven.*

Here's our cake so nice and round.
> *Make a circle with arms.*

We frost it pink and white.
> *Action of spreading frosting.*

We put four candles on it,
> *Hold up four fingers.*

To make a birthday bright.

Birthday Candles

Today I have a birthday.
I'm four years old, you see.
> *Hold up four fingers.*

And here I have a birthday cake
> *Make circle with arms.*

Which you may share with me.
> *Point to friend in group.*

First we count the candles,

Count them, every one.

One, two, three, four,
> *Hold up fingers one by one.*

The counting now is done.

Let's blow out the candles.

Out each flame will go.

"Wh ..., wh ..., wh ..., wh ...,"
> *Pretend to blow out candles.*

As one by one we blow.
> *Bend down fingers one at a time.*

Body Parts

by Chuck Schacht, Romeo, MI

My parts are big.
> *Stretch arms way out.*

My parts are small
> *Bring index fingers close together.*

There's parts that help me taste and
crawl.
> *Point to tongue and knees.*

There's parts that help me touch and
see.
> *Touch fingers and eyes.*

I know all the parts of me.
> *(Then have children identify other body parts not mentioned in the rhyme.)*

Boom, Bang!

Boom, bang, boom, bang!
Bang gong.

Rumpety, lumpety, bump!
Beat drum.

Zoom, zam, zoom, zam!
Cut back and forth with hands.

Clippety, clappety, clump!
*Nod head from side to side in rhythm
with words.*

Rustles and bustles

And swishes and zings!
Hug shoulders, rock in rhythm.

What wonderful noises

A thunderstorm brings!

Una Boquita
(A Little Mouth)

Una boquita para comer.
(My little mouth to eat.)
Point to mouth.

Mi naricita es para oler.
(My little nose to sniff.)
Point to nose.

Mis dos ojitos son para ver.
(My two little eyes to see.)
Point to eye.

Mis dos oídos son para oír.
(My two ears to hear.)
Point to ears.

¿Y me cabecita? Para dormir.
(And my little head? To sleep.)
Lean head on hands, as if to sleep.

Brownies

This little elf likes to hammer.
Hold up thumb. Pretend to hammer.

This little elf likes to saw.
Hold up index finger. Pretend to saw.

This little elf likes to splash or paint.
Hold up tall finger. Motion of painting.

This one has pictures to draw.
Hold up ring finger. Motion of drawing.

And this little elf likes best of all
Hold up little finger.

To put the cry in the baby doll.
Bend and cry, "Mama, Mama."

Brushing Teeth

Up and down and round and round
Pretend to brush.

I brush my teeth to keep them sound;
Point to teeth.

To keep them sound and clean and
white
I brush them morning, noon and
night.

Bubble, Hop, and Stop
by Theresa A. Miller, O'Fallon, MO

One bubble, 2 bubbles, 3 bubbles, top.
Tap head once.

4 bubbles, 5 bubbles, 6 bubbles, hop.
Hop once.

7 bubbles, 8 bubbles, 9 bubbles, pop.
Clap hands once.

10 bubbles float down, time to stop.
Sit down.

Buenos Días
(Good Morning)

Buenos días, hermanos míos.
(Good morning, my brothers.)
Hold up left hand.

Contento dice Pulgar,
("I am happy," says the thumb,)
Point to thumb.

Índice y Dedo del Medio,
(The index finger and the middle
finger,)
Point to index and middle fingers.

Se inclinan a saludar.
(They bow deeply to say hello.)
*Bend those three fingers while holding
down ring finger with thumb.*

El Anular muy sonriente
(The ring finger smiles broadly and
bows)
Point to ring finger.

Una caravana hará

Y el Meñique consentido
(And the spoiled little finger)
Point to little finger

Su cabeza inclinará.
(Just nods his head.)
Bend those two fingers down.

Building a Snowman

I will build a snowman;
Pretend to roll snow.

Make him big and tall.
Pile snow on top of other snow.

See if you can hit him

With a big snowball.
Make and throw snowballs.

Bullfrog

Here's Mr. Bullfrog
Left hand closed, thumb upright.

Sitting on a rock.

Along comes a little boy.
Walking motion with right hand.

Mr. Bullfrog jumps, KERPLOP!
Tuck thumb into closed hand.

Bunnies

Out in the garden
Point to the right.

Where the cabbages grow,
Form large circle with arms.

Happy little cotton tails
Hold up five fingers of left hand.

Are hopping to and fro.
*Raise fingers in up and down
movement.*

Along comes a puppy dog

Looking for some fun,
Make fingers of right hand creep.

"Bow-wow-wow," he barks,

And off the bunnies run.
*Hand representing bunnies hops rapidly
away.*

Bunny Bows

by Marie Noe, Abilene, TX

Oh dear, Oh dear! What shall we do?
Put hands to face and shake head.

Someone needs to tie his shoe!
Point to shoe.

Take each lace, one left, one right,
Grab laces.

Loop them 'round and pull them tight.
Make 1st loop and tighten.

Make two loops, (now this is funny).
Make loops and whisper.

One's a tree and one's a bunny!
Wiggle each loop on cue.

Run the bunny 'round the tree,
Run right loop around left.

That will make a hole, you see.
Show hole formed at base of loops.

Stick the bunny through that spot.
Put "bunny" loop in hole.

Pull both loops to make your knot!
Pull loops to tighten.

And that is all you have to do
To make a bunny tie your shoe!

Busy Fingers

(Tune: "Here We Go 'Round the Mulberry Bush.")

This is the way my fingers stand,
Fingers stand, fingers stand,
This is the way my fingers stand,
So early in the morning.

This is the way they dance about,
Dance about, dance about,
This is the way they dance about,
So early in the morning.

This is the way I fold my hands,
Fold my hands, fold my hands,
This is the way I fold my hands,
So early in the morning.

This is the way they go to rest,
Go to rest, go to rest,
This is the way they go to rest,
Cup hands loosely, palms up and place in lap.

So early in the morning.

Suit action to words.

Busy Hands

Hands on shoulders, hands on knees,
Put them behind you, if you please.
Raise hands high up in the air,
Down at your sides, now touch your
    hair.
Hands at side now you may place,
Touch your elbows, now your face.
Raise hands high up as before,
Now you may clap 1, 2, 3, 4.
Now sit down, hands folded once
    more.
Eyes to the front, feet on the floor.

Suit actions to words.

By Gum! By Gum!

If I move one finger and wiggle my
    thumb,
I'll have two fingers moving, by gum!
    Clap hands.

By gum!
    Clap hands.

If I move two fingers and wiggle both
    thumbs,
I'll have four fingers moving, by gum!
    Clap hands.

By gum!
    Clap hands.
    Continue through all ten fingers.

If I move both arms and wiggle my
    thumbs,
I'll have arms and thumbs moving, by
    gum!
    Clap hands.

By gum!
    Clap hands.

If I move both feet and wiggle my
    thumbs,
I'll have feet and thumbs moving, by
    gum!
    Clap hands

By gum!
    Clap Hands.

If I stand up, sit down and wiggle my
    thumbs,
I'll get very tired and I'll quit, by gum!
    Clap hands

By gum!
    Clap hands.

C

Captain and His Men

One, two, three, four, five in a row,
Pop up fingers one at a time.

A captain and his men!
And on the other side, you know,
Are six, seven, eight, nine, ten.
Pop up other fingers one at a time.

Chick Ways

When a little chicken eats,
He scampers all around,
Picking here and picking there,
Bits of dinner from the ground.
Pecking motions with one hand on the other.

When a little chicken drinks,
He stands so very still,
While the water trickles down
Through his upturned bill.
Hold head up — fingers of right hand trickle down throat.

The Caterpillar

A caterpillar crawled to the top of a tree.
Index finger of left hand moves up right arm in crawling motion.

"I think I'll take a nap," said he.

So — under a leaf he began to creep
Wrap right hand over left fist.

To spin his cocoon, and he fell asleep.

All winter he slept in his cocoon bed,
Keep right hand closed over left fist.

'Till spring came along one day and said,

"Wake up, wake up, little sleepyhead.
Shake left fist with right hand.

Wake up, it's time to get out of bed."

So — he opened his eyes that sun shiny day.
Spread fingers and look into hand.

Lo! He was a butterfly — and flew away!
Move hand in flying motion.

The Chinese Fan

Sit on the floor with legs straight out.

A ship sailed from China with a
cargo of tea,

All laden with presents for you and for
me.

They brought me a fan.

Just imagine my bliss

When I fan myself daily, like this, like
this,

Like this, like this.

Repeat five times. Each time "like this" is said, fan yourself as follows:

1st time: Four times with your right hand in rhythm.

2nd time: Four times with both hands.

3rd time: Four times with both hands as you sweep your right foot up and over your left foot in rhythm.

4th time: Four times with both hands as you sweep your right foot across the left, then the left across the right in rhythm.

5th time: Four times with both hands, both feet, as you nod your head forward and backward.

Choo-Choo Train

This is a choo-choo train
Bend arms at elbows.

Puffing down the track.
Rotate forearms in rhythm.

Now it's going forward,
Push arms foreward; continue rotating.

Now it's going back.
Pull arms back; continue rotating.

Now the bell is ringing,
Pull bell cord with closed fist.

Now the whistle blows.
Hold fist near mouth and blow.

What a lot of noise it makes
Cover ears with hands.

Everywhere it goes.
Stretch out arms.

Christmas Presents

See all the presents by the Christmas tree,
> *Hands in sweeping motion.*

Some for you,
> *Point to neighbor.*

And some for me.
> *Point to self.*

Long ones,
> *Show width with two hands.*

Tall ones,
> *Measure with hand from floor.*

Short ones, too,
> *Measure shortness.*

And here is a round one
> *Make circle with arms.*

Wrapped in blue.

Isn't it fun to look and see
> *Nodding head.*

All of the presents by the Christmas tree.

Christmas Time

> (This can be sung to the tune of "Row, Row, Row your Boat.")

Ring, ring, ring the bells,
> *Make motions of bells ringing.*

Ring them loud and clear,

To tell the children everywhere

That Christmas time is here.

Chubby Little Snowman

A chubby little snowman had a carrot nose.
> *Form snowman with right fist, with thumb sticking out for nose.*

Along came a bunny, and what do you suppose?
> *Use two fingers of the left hand to hop toward snowman.*

That hungry little bunny, looking for his lunch,

Ate that snowman's carrot nose,
> *Bunny grabs snowman's nose.*

Nibble, nibble, crunch!

The Church

Here is the church,
> *Laced fingers.*

And here is the steeple.
> *Index fingers together at tips.*

Open the door,
> *Spread hands.*

And see all the people.

Here is the parson
> *Index finger makes walking motion.*

Going upstairs.

And here he is

Saying his prayers.
> *Fold hands in prayer.*

A Churning We Will Go

(Tune of "A Hunting We Will Go")

Ohhh — a churning we will go,
A churning wc will go.
We'll take the cream
And shake it so
And get the butter, OHHHHH!!!!

Suit actions to words.

Cinco Calabacitas

(Five Little Pumpkins.)

Cinco calabacitas sentadas en un
  portón.
(Five little pumpkins sitting on a
  gate;)

*Cross hands and use one hand, 5 fingers
for five pumpkins.*

La primera dijo:
(The first one said,)
Hold up finger.

"Se está haciendo tarde."
("My, it's getting late.")

La segunda dijo:
(The second one said,)
Hold up second finger.

"Hay brujas en el aire."
("There are witches in the air.")

La tercera dijo:
(The third one said,)
Hold up third finger.

"No le hace."
("But we don't care.")

La cuarta dijo:
(The fourth one said,)
Hold up fourth finger.

"¡Corramos, corramos!"
("Let's run, let's run.")

La quinta dijo:
(The fifth one said,)
Hold up thumb.

"Es una noche de espanto."
("It's Halloween fun.")

Uuuu hizo el viento
("WOOOOOOOO," went the
  wind,)
Wave arms.

Y se apagaron las luces.
(And out went the lights.)
Clap.

Las cinco calabacitas
(These five little pumpkins)

Corrieron a esconderse!
(Ran fast out of sight.)
Run fingers behind back.

Cinco Pollitos

(Five Chicks)

Cinco pollitos
Tiene mi tía,
(My aunt has five chicks.)
Extend five fingers on one hand.

Uno le canta,
(One sings to her,)
First raise index finger.

Otro le pía,
(The other peeps,)
Raise middle finger.

Y tres le tocan
(And three play)
Then all five fingers are extended again.

La chirimía.
(The *chirimia.*)

Clap Your Hands

Clap your hands, 1,2, 3.

Clap your hands just like me.

Roll your hands, 1,2, 3.

Roll your hands just like me.

Suit actions to words.

The Clock

With a tick and a tock,

And a tick and a tock,

The clock goes round all day.

It tells us when it's time to work,

And when it's time to play.

Move arm as a pendulum, hand upraised and elbow resting in cupped other hand. Click tongue in time to movement.

Clocks

Big clocks make a sound like

T-i-c-k, t-o-c-k, t-i-c-k, t-o-c-k.

Rest elbows on hips; extend forearms and index fingers up and move arms sideways slowly and rhythmically.

Small clocks make a sound like

Tick, tock, tick, tock,

Move arms faster.

And the very tiny clocks make a sound

Like tick, tick, tock, tock.

Move still faster.

Tick, tock, tick, tock, tick, tock.

Cobbler, Cobbler

Cobbler, cobbler, mend my shoe.

Right fist pounds on left fist.

Have it done by half past two.

Stitch it up, stitch it down,

Make stitches with right hand.

Make the very best shoes in town.

Los Cochintos
(The Little Pigs)

Éste compró un huevo,
(This one bought an egg.)

Éste encendió el fuego,
(This one started the fire.)

Éste trajo la sal,
(This one brought the salt.)

Éste lo guisó,
(This one cooked it.)

Y este pícaro gordo se lo comió.
(And this little chubby one ate it all up.)

Point to each finger on one hand for every line. Begin with little finger, end with thumb.

Contando y Cantando
(Counting and Singing)

Uno, dos, tres, cuatro y cinco,
(One, two, three, four and five

Seis, siete, ocho, nueve y diez.
(Six, seven,eight, nine and ten.)
Extend one finger after another.

Con esta mano cuento cinco
(With this hand I count five)
Show left hand.

Y con esta otra hasta diez.
(And with this other hand, up to ten.)
Show right hand.

Counting
by Don K. Savelle, Charleston, SC

Eeny, meeny, miney, moe
Clap on each word.

I count fast and I count slow.
Hands on hips.

1 -2 -3 -4- 5
Show one finger with each number.

Watch my fingers come alive!
6 - 7 - 8- 9 - 10

Want to hear me count again?
Fold arms across chest.

The Cows

Here is the barn so big, don't you see?
Make large circle with finger tips together.

In walk the cows, one, two, three.
Push the finger of the right hand in through the spread fingers of the left hand.

Soon there'll be milk for you and me.
Point to group, and then yourself.

Creeping

Creeping, creeping, creeping,
Creep fingers up the other arm.

Comes the little cat.

But bunny with his long ears
Hop fingers of one hand up the other arm.

Hops like that!

The Crocodile

She sailed away on a lovely summer's day,

On the back of a crocodile.
Place right hand on back of left with right fingers even with left palm.

"You see," said she,

"It's as plain as plain can be,

I'll go sailing down the Nile."
Move in swaying motion.

The croc winked his eye,
Wink.

As she waved them all good-bye,
Wave.

Wearing a happy smile.
Smile.

At the end of the ride,

The lady was inside,
Use two hands, with base of palms together, open and shut.

And the smile on the crocodile.

¿Cuántos Dedos?
(How Many Fingers?)

Retintín retintón
(Retintin, retinton)
> *Show hands with fingers extended.*

¿Cuántos? ¿Cuántos dedos son?
(How many? How many fingers are
   there?)

Cup of Tea

Here's a cup
> *Form cup with one hand.*

And here's a cup,
> *Form cup with other hand.*

And here's a pot of tea.
> *Form tea pot with both hands.*

Pour a cup,
> *Pouring motion.*

And pour a cup,

And have a drink with me.
> *Pretend to drink.*

D

Day At the Beach

Ocean breeze blowing,
Sway arms back and forth.

Feet kick and splash,
Kick feet.

Ocean waves breaking

On rocks with a crash.
Clap hands loudly.

Boys finding seashells,
Look toward ground — pick up shell.

Girls sifting sand,
Pretend to sift sand.

Friends building castles
*Place one hand on top of other —
continue going higher.*

As high as they can.

I stretch my arms out
Stretch arms out to sides.

Far as they'll reach.

Oh, my! What fun

On this day at the beach.

A Delicious Cake

Mix the batter,
Make motion of stirring.

Stir the batter,

Shake some flour in.

Mix the batter,

Stir the batter,
Make shaking motion with one hand.

Place it in a tin.
Make motion of pouring into pan.

Sprinkle little raisins on,
*With one hand make motion of
sprinkling raisins on batter.*

Pop batter in to bake.
Make motions of placing cake in oven.

Open wide the oven door,
*Bend down and make motion as if
opening oven door.*

And out comes a cake!

Did You Feed My Cow?

Did you feed my cow?
  Yes, ma'am!

Will you tell me how?
  Yes, ma'am!

Oh, what did you give her?
  Corn and hay.

Oh, what did you give her?
  Corn and hay.

Did you milk her good?
  Yes, ma'am!

Did you do like you should?
  Yes, ma'am!

Oh, how did you milk her?
  Swish! Swish! Swish!

Oh, how did you milk her?
  Swish! Swish! Swish!

Did my cow get sick!
  Yes, ma'am!

Was she covered with tick!
  Yes, ma'am!

Oh, how was she sick?
  All bloated up.

Oh, how was she sick?
  All bloated up.

Did my cow die?
  Yes, ma'am!

Did my cow die?
  Yes, ma'am!

Oh how did she die?
  Ugh! Ugh! Ugh!

Oh how did she die?
  Ugh! Ugh! Ugh!

Did the buzzards come?
  Yes, ma'am!

For to pick her bones?
  Yes, ma'am!

Oh, how did they come?
  Flop! Flop! Flop!

Oh, how did they come?
  Flop! Flop! Flop!

> *Leader chants the question (first line);*
> *children answer in rhythm (second line).*
> *Do appropriate movements.*

Diez Gallinitas*
(Ten Little Chickens)

Cinco huevitos
(Five little eggs)
> *Show one hand with fingers extended.*

Y cinco huevitos son diez.
(And five little eggs are ten.)
> *Show the other hand.*

La gallina se pone
(The hen)
> *Lay one hand on top of the other, palms*
> *together.*

Sobre de ellos otra vez.
(Sits on them again.)

Pío, pío, pío.
(Peep, peep, peep)

¿Qué ves?
(What do you see?)

Diez pollitos esta vez.
(Ten little chicks, I see.)
> *Show ten fingers again.*

*See "Ten Fluffy Chickens."

Dos Pajaritos*
(Two Little Birds)

Dos pajaritos muy sentados
(Two little birds)
> *Extend two index fingers.*

En una cerca muy alta;
(Sitting on a fence;)

Vuela Panchito, vuela Pedrito.
(Panchito flys away, Pedrito flys away.)
> *Fly hands behind back.*

Vuelve Panchito, vuelve Pedrito.
(Panchito returns, Pedrito returns.)
> *Return hands to front with index finger*
> *still extended.*

*See "Two Little Black Birds."

The Doughnut

Here's the doughnut,
> *Circle with index fingers and thumbs.*

Big and round and fat.

Here's the hole,
> *Make circle with index finger and*
> *thumb of one hand.*

Now don't eat that.

Draw a Circle

Draw a circle, draw a circle,
> *Draw a circle with pointer finger.*

Round as can be;

Draw a circle, draw a circle

Just for me.
> *Point to self.*

Draw a square, draw a square,
> *Draw a square in the air.*

Shaped like a door;

Draw a square, draw a square

With corners four.

Draw a triangle, draw a triangle,
> *Draw a triangle in the air.*

With corners three;

Draw a triangle, draw a triangle

Just for me.
> *Point to self.*

E

Easter

Easter is a happy time;
All the flowers are growing.
Make circles cups with hands.

In the nest the birdies sing;
Put hands together to form nest.

In the church, the church bells ring.
Pretend to ring bell.

Easter Bunny

Easter Bunny's ears are floppy.
*Place hands on each side of head. Make
them flop.*

Easter Bunny's feet are hoppy.
Feet hop.

His fur is soft,
Stroke arm.

And nose is fluffy,
Touch nose.

Tail is short and powder-puffy.
Form tail with hands behind.

Eency Weency Spider

An eency weency spider
Climbed up the water spout.
One hand climbs up arm to shoulder.

Down came the rain
*Raise hands high in air and drop them
down quickly.*

And washed the spider out.
Hand slides down arm.

Out came the sun
Arms form circle over head.

And dried up all the rain.
The eency, weency spider
Climbed up the spout again.
Hand goes back up arm to shoulder.

Los Elefantes
(The Elephants)

Un elefante se balanceaba
(An elephant balanced)
> *Extend one finger.*

Sobre la tela de una araña.
(On a spider web.)
> *Swing arms together as elephant trunk.*

Cuando veía como resistía
(When he saw how strong it was)

Fue a llamar a otro elefante.
(He called another elephant over.)

Dos elefantes se balanceaban
(Two elephants balanced)
> *Extend two fingers.*

Sobre la tela de una araña.
(On a spider web.)
> *Elephant trunk motion.*

Cuando veían como resistía
(When they saw how strong it was)

Fueron a llamar a otro elefante.
(They called another elephant over.)

Tres...
(Three elephants...)
> *Extend three fingers.*

Cuatro...
(Four elephants ...)
> *Extend four fingers.*

Cinco...
(Five elephants ...)
> *Extend five fingers, etc...*

Elephant

Right foot, left foot, see me go.
> *Put weight on first one foot, then the other, swaying from side to side.*

I am grey and big and slow.
I come walking down the street
With my trunk and four big feet.
> *Extend arms together in front and swing like a trunk.*

The Engine

Here is an engine
That runs on this track.

It whistles – "Toot Toot"

And then it runs back.
> *Use left arm for track and right hand for engine that runs up and down.*

Enumeration

I have five fingers on each hand,
> *Hold up both hands with fingers
> outspread.*

Ten toes on both my feet;
> *Point to feet.*

Two ears, two eyes, one nose, one
mouth,
> *Point to each.*

With which to gently speak.

My hands can clap,
> *Clap hands.*

My feet can tap,
> *Tap feet.*

My eyes can brightly shine.
> *Point to eyes with both index fingers.*

My ears can hear,
> *Cup hands to ears.*

My nose can smell,
> *Point to nose and sniff.*

My mouth can speak a rhyme.
> *Point to mouth.*

Éste
(This One)

Éste se halló un huevito
(This little finger found an egg.)

Éste lo quebró,
(This one broke it.)

Éste lo frió,
(This one fried it.)

Éste le echó sal,
(This one put salt on it.)

Y este viejo gordo se lo comió.
(And this old fat one ate it all up.)

> *This finger play is like "This Little Pig
> Went to Market." Start with little
> finger.*

Exercise Song

I'll put my hands in my lap,

My feet together so;

I'll sit up straight as straight can be,

For that is right, you know.

I'll stand up straight and tall,

Hands at my side, just so;

I'll look in front and do the thing

That is just right, you know.

I'll march and march around,

With steps just fast or slow;

I'll make no noise as I go 'round,

For this is right, you know.

> *Suit actions to words.*

Eye Winker

Eye Winker,
> *Point to eyes.*

Tom Tinker,
> *Point to ears.*

Nose Smeller,
> *Point to nose.*

Mouth Eater,
> *Point to mouth.*

Chin Chopper,
> *Tap chin.*

Chin Chopper, Chin Chopper,

Chin Chopper, Chin.

Eyes to See With

Eyes to see with,
Ears to hear with,
Nose to smell with,
Teeth to chew.
Feet to run with,
Hands to work with,
I'm a lucky child,
Aren't you?

     Suit action to words

F

The Fairies' Wash Day

This is the fairies' wash day,
With acorn cups for tubs,
Cup hands.

And tiny leaves for wash boards,
Show palms.

Each fairy rubs and rubs.
Motion of scrubbing.

The fairy sheets so white and fine
Upon the grass are lying.
Motion of spreading.

The spider spins a line for them,
Twirl finger.

And now the clothes are drying.

Falling Raindrops

Raindrops, raindrops!
Move fingers to imitate falling rain.

Falling all around.

Pitter-patter on the rooftops,
Tap softly on floor.

Pitter-patter on the ground.
Repeat.

Here is my umbrella.
Pretend to open umbrella.

It will keep me dry.
Place over head.

When I go walking in the rain
I hold it up so high.
Hold high in air.

La Familia
(The Family)

Esta es la mamá gordita y bonita.
(This is the mother, pretty and fat.)
> *Point to the thumb.*

Este es el papá que va a trabajar.
(This is the father that goes to work.)
> *Point to index finger.*

Este es el niño que le gusta ayudar.
(This is the little boy that likes to
   help.)
> *Point to middle finger.*

Este es la niña que le gusta estudiar.
(This is the little girl that likes to
   study.)
> *Point to ring finger.*

Este es el bebé que le gusta jugar.
(And this is the little baby that likes to
   play.)
> *Point to baby finger.*

Farmer and His Seeds
(Tune: "Farmer in the Dell.")

The farmer plants the seeds,
The farmer plants the seeds,
> *Children pretend to plant seeds.*

Hi, Ho, the dairy-o,
The farmer plants the seeds.

The sun comes out to shine, etc.
> *Make large circle with arms.*

The rain begins to fall, etc.
> *Hands flutter up and down.*

The seeds begin to grow, etc.
> *Children begin to rise.*

The farmer cuts them down, etc.
> *Move arms to imitate a mower.*

He binds them into sheaves, etc.
> *Children group together.*

And now we'll have some bread.
> *Pretend to eat.*

Farmer Plows the Ground

(Tune — "Here We Go 'Round the Mulberry Bush.")

First the farmer plows the ground,
Guide plow down the rows.

Plows the ground, plows the ground.

First the farmer plows the ground,

Then he plants the seeds.
Plant seeds.

This is the way he plants the seeds,...
Children in a crouched position.

So that they will grow.

The rain and sun will help them grow,...
Children begin to rise.

Right up through the ground.

Now the farmer picks the beans,...
Leader pretends to pick children. Other foods could be substituted.

And we have food to eat.

The Farmyard

In the farmyard at the end of the day,

All the animals politely say,

"Thank you for my food today."

The cow says, "Moo."
Point to thumb.

The pigeon, "Coo."
Point to index finger.

The sheep says, "Baa."
Point to middle finger.

The lamb says, "Maaa."
Point to fourth finger.

The hen, "Cluck, cluck, cluck."
Point to little finger.

"Quack," says the duck.
Point to the various fingers of the opposite hand for remaining animals.

The dog, "Bow wow."

The cat, "Meow."

The horse, "Neigh."

The pig grunts, "Oink."

Then the barn is locked up tight

And the farmer says, "Good Night."
Hands together against cheek.

A Fat Bunny

A fat bunny rabbit with ears so tall,
Place hands on head to form ears.

And two pink eyes about this small,
Form two circles with thumbs and index fingers.

Went hop, hop, hopping to get some lunch.

He found a fresh carrot,
Suit the rest of actions to words.

O yum-yum, crunch-crunch!

While he was eating and having such fun,

Bang! What a noise! He started to run.

All you could see as he went racing by,

Was his powder puff tail — waving good-bye.

Fee, Fie, Foe, Fum

Fee, fie, fo, fum,
Point to little finger for "fee." Continue with other fingers.

See my finger,
Point to index finger.

See my thumb.
Point to thumb.

Fee, fie, fo, fum,
Repeat first instructions.

Fingers gone,
Hide finger in hand.

So is thumb.
Hide thumb.

The Finger Band

(Sing to "Here We Go 'Round the Mulberry Bush.")

The Finger Band is coming to town,
Fingers behind back, speaking softly, gradually louder as they are brought to the front.

Coming to town, coming to town.

The Finger Band is coming to town,

So early in the morning.

This the way they wear their hats,...
Hands on head to show hats.

This is the way they wave their flags,...
Waving motion with hands.

This is the way they beat their drums,...
Beating motion with hands.

This is the way they blow their horns,...
Hands to mouth in blowing motion.

The Finger Band is going away,

Going away, going away.

The Finger Band is going away,

So early in the morning.
As fingers are gradually moved behind back, sound becomes softer.

Finger Family

This is the mother, as nice as can be.
Index finger.

This is the father, the tallest is he.
Middle finger.

This is the brother, he's growing up tall.
Ring finger.

Here's Grandma and Grandpa, and
Thumbs.

I love them all.

Fingers

Fingers, fingers, everywhere!
Fingers blinking in the air.
Fingers making little holes.
Fingers tying little bows.
Fingers learning to button and snap.
Fingers on hands that like to clap.

Suit action to words.

The Fish

I hold my fingers like a fish,
Place one hand on top of the other.

And wave them as I go.
Waving motion with hands.

See them swimming with a swish,
Swimming motion with hands.

So swiftly to and fro.

Five Brown Pennies

Five brown pennies in my purse;
Hold up five fingers.

This one's for some gum.
Point to thumb.

This one's for a lollipop,
Point to pointer finger.

This one's for a drum.
Point to middle finger.

These I'll save inside my purse,
Point to ring and little fingers.

Until your birthday comes.

Five Fingers

Five fingers on this hand,
Hold up one hand.

Five fingers on that;
Hold up other hand.

A dear little nose,
Point to nose.

A mouth like a rose,
Point to mouth.

Two cheeks so tiny and fat.
Point to each cheek.

Two eyes, two ears,
Point to each.

And ten little toes;
Point to toes.

That's the way the baby grows.

Five Little Bells

Five little bells, hanging in a row.

The first one said, "Ring me slow."

The second one said, "Ring me fast."

The third one said, "Ring me last."

The fourth one said, "I'm like a chime."

The fifth one said, "Ring me at Christmas Time."

Hold up five fingers and bend them down one at a time as verse progresses.

Five Little Birds

Five little birds without any home;
Raise left hand fingers.

Five little trees in a row.
Raise right hand fingers.

Come build your nests
Fingers of both hands interlaced.

In our branches tall,

We'll rock you to and fro.
Sway nest gently.

Five Little Chickadees

Five little chickadees

Peeping at the door;

One flew away,

And then there were four.

Four little chickadees

Sitting on a tree;

One flew away,

And then there were three.

Three little chickadees

Looking at you;

One flew away,

And then there were two.

Two little chickadees

Sitting in the sun;

One flew away,

And then there was one.

One little chickadee

Left all alone;

One flew away,

And then there was none.

Hold up five fingers and bend them down, one at a time as verse progresses.

Five Little Easter Eggs

Five little Easter eggs,
Hold up five fingers.

Lovely colors wore;

Mother ate the blue one,
Bend down one finger.

Then there were four.
Hold up four fingers.

Four little Easter eggs,

Two and two, you see;
Point to two at a time.

Daddy ate the red one,
Bend down second finger.

Then there were three.
Hold up three fingers.

Three little Easter eggs;
Hold up three fingers.

Before I knew,

Sister ate the yellow one,
Bend down third finger.

Then there were two.
Hold up two fingers.

Two little Easter eggs,

Oh, what fun!

Brother ate the purple one,
Bend down fourth finger.

Then there was one.
Hold up one finger.

One little Easter egg;
Hold up one finger.

See me run!

I ate the last one.
Motion with hands to signify none.

And then there was none.

Five Little Elephants

Five little elephants
Rowing toward the shore;
One fell in,
Then there were four.

Four little elephants
Climbing up a tree;
One slid down,
Then there were three.

Three little elephants
Living in the zoo;
One walked off,
Then there were two.

Two little elephants
Playing in the sun;
One fell asleep,
Then there was one.

One little elephant
Isn't any fun;
Abra-ca-da-bra!
Then there were none!

Holding up five fingers, suit actions to words.

Five Little Eskimos

by Pam Earhart, Flint, MI

Five little Eskimos by the igloo door,

One went out to feed the dogs, then
there were four.

Four little Eskimos rowing out to sea,

One jumped on an iceberg, then there
were three.

Three little Eskimos making fish stew,

One burned his finger, then there were
two.

Two little Eskimos hunting just for
fun,

One chased a baby seal, then there was
one.

One little Eskimo all his work done,

Went home to supper, then there were
none.

> *Hold up all fingers and push down one
> by one.*

Five Little Farmers

Five little farmers,
> *Fingers of one hand closed tightly over
> thumb.*

Woke up with the sun,
> *Open hand, with fingers and thumb
> standing upright.*

For it was early morning

And chores must be done.

The first little farmer

Went to milk the cow.
> *Making milking motion.*

The second little farmer

Thought he'd better plow.
> *Hold plow; move hand to right and left.*

The third little farmer

Fed the hungry hens.
> *Hold feed in left hand, toss out with
> right.*

The fourth little farmer

Mended broken pens.
> *Make hammer of fist, pound.*

The fifth little farmer

Took his vegetables to town,
> *Riding motion.*

Baskets filled with cabbages

And sweet potatoes, brown.

When the work was finished
and the western sky was red,
> *Sweep arm across sky.*

Five little farmers tumbled into bed.
> *Clasp right hand in left.*

Five Little Firemen

Five little firemen sit very still
Bend fingers down one at a time.

Until they see a fire on the hill.

Number one rings the bell, ding-dong!

Number two pulls his big boots on.

Number three jumps on the fire
engine red,

Number four puts a hat on his head.

Number five drives the truck to the
fire,

As the big, yellow flames go higher
and higher.
Spread arms.

"Whooooo-ooooo! Whooooo-ooooo!"
hear the fire truck say.

As all of the cars get out of the way.

Shhhhhh! goes the water from the fire
hose spout,
Rub palms together.

And quicker than a wink the fire is
out!
Clap hands.

Five Little Goblins

Five little goblins on a Halloween
night,

Made a very, very spooky sight.

First one danced on his tippy-tip-toes.

The next one tumbled and bumped
his nose.

The next one jumped high up in the
air.

The next one walked like a fuzzy bear.

The next one sang a Halloween song.

Five goblins played the whole night
long!

Bend fingers down one at a time.

Five Little Fishes

Five little fishes were swimming near
the shore;
*Hold up five fingers and bend down one
as at a time.*

One took a dive, then there were four.

Four little fishes were swimming out
to sea;

One went for food, then there were
three.

Three little fishes said, "Now what
shall we do?"

One swam away, and then there were
two.

Two little fishes were having great fun;

But one took a plunge, then there was
one.

One little fish said, "I like the warm
sun."

Away he went and then there were
none.
Put hand behind back.

Five Little Mice

Five little mice came out to play,
Fingers of right hand run forward.

Gathering crumbs along the way.
*Fingers stop once in a while then
continue to move.*

Out comes a pussy cat,
*Close three middle fingers of left hand
and raise thumb and little finger.*

Sleek and fat.

Four little mice

Went scampering back.
*Tuck thumb of right hand under and
let other four fingers run back.*

Five Little Monkeys

Five little monkeys jumping on the
    bed,
    Five fingers jumping.

One fell off and bumped his head.
    Put one finger down.

Mother called the doctor and the
    doctor said,
    Pretend to phone.

"No more monkeys jumping on the
    bed!"
    Shaking finger for "No More..."

    Repeat: Four little monkeys...

Five Little Ponies

Five little ponies all dapple gray;
    *Hold up five fingers. Bend them down
    as verse progresses.*

Down in the meadow not far away.

The first one said, "Let's run, Let's
    run!"

The second one said, "Oh, that's no
    fun."

The third one said, "I'm going to
    neigh."

The fourth one said, "I'd like some
    hay."

The fifth one said, "Here comes a
    jeep."

So the five little ponies away did leap.
    Fingers leap behind back.

Five Little Pigs

This little pig makes an "oink, oink"
    sound,

This little pig is fat and round.

This little pig roots all around,

With his piggy snout, he digs up the
    ground.

This little pig has a curly tail.

He eats his lunch from a shiny pail.

This little pig doesn't seem to care

If any of the other pigs get their share.
    *Hold up five fingers and bend each
    down as verse progresses.*

Five Little Pumpkins*

Five little pumpkins sitting on a gate;
    Hold up five fingers.

The first one said, "My, it's getting
    late."

The second one said, "There are
    witches in the air."

The third one said, "But we don't
    care."

The fourth one said, "Let's run, let's
    run."

The fifth one said, "It's Halloween
    fun."

"WOOOOOOOO" went the wind,
    Sway hand through the air.

And out went the lights.
    Loud clap.

And away they all ran on Halloween
    night.
    Place hands behind back.

*See "Cinco Calabacitas."

Five Little Robins

Five little robins lived in a tree.
Father,
Thumb.

Mother,
Little finger.

And babies three.
Three fingers.

Father caught a worm.
Catching motion.

Mother caught a bug.
The three little robins
Began to tug.
Tugging motion.

This one got a bug.

This one got a worm.

This one said, "Now it's my turn."

Five Little Snowmen

Five little snowmen, happy and gay;
*Hold up five fingers. Bend down one at
a time as verse progresses.*

The first one said, "What a lovely
day."

The second one said, "We'll never
have tears."

The third one said, "We'll stay for
years."

The fourth one said, "But what
happens in May?"

The fifth one said, "Look, we're
melting away."
Children gradually 'melt' to floor.

Five Little Valentines

Five little valentines from the grocery
store;

I sent one to Mother, now there are
four.

Four little valentines, pretty ones to
see;

I gave one to Brother, now there are
three.

Three little valentines, yellow, red and
blue;

I gave one to Sister, now there are two.

Two little valentines, my we have fun;

I gave one to Daddy, now there is one.

One little valentine, the story is almost
done;

I gave it to Baby, now there are none.
*Hold up five fingers and bend them
down one at a time as verse progresses.*

Five Soldiers

Five little soldiers standing in a row;
Hold up five fingers of right hand.

Three stood straight, and two stood
so.
Right thumb folds forefinger down.

Along came the captain, and what do
you think?
Other three fingers stand up.

Up jumped the other two, quick as a
wink.
All fingers pop up.

The Five Vultures

by Linda L. Plevak. Reprinted with permission.

Five black vultures
Hold up five fingers

Sitting on a wire;
The first one says,
Hold up one finger.

"I think I'll retire."
Cradle hands under head.

The second one says,
Hold up two fingers.

"C'mon let's eat."
Wave "C'mon."

The third one says,
Hold up three fingers.

"We must wait for the heat."
Shake finger to warn.

The fourth one opens
Hold up four fingers.

His wings to dry.
Extend arms.

The fifth one waits
Hold up five fingers.

For an animal to die.
Put fists under chin as in waiting.

The air warms up,
And the vultures take a dip.
Make a circle sun. Then dip hand.

They glide on the thermals,
Like a sailing ship.
Use hand to glide.

They land by an animal
That's been dead for a day.
Land hand on lap.

But for the five vultures,
That's okay.
Nod head "yes."

'Cause the vulture's claws
Make claws with hands.

Are not made to kill
So they find something dead,
Then eat their fill.
Make binocular eyes. Rub tummy.

We may not think
They are careful selectors.
Shake head "No."

But vultures are nature's
Garbage collectors.
Hands upward, "That's how it is!"

Five Wooden Soldiers

Five wooden soldiers standing in a
    row;
Look out! Look out! Down they go!
Down goes little man,
Down goes ring man,
Down goes middle man,
Down goes pointer,
Down goes thumbkin.
All five soldiers, lying just so!

*Hold up five fingers. Bend down one at
a time as verse progresses starting with
the little finger.*

The Flower

Here's a green leaf,
Show hand.

And here's a green leaf;
Show other hand.

That, you see, makes two.
Hold up two fingers.

Here is a bud
Cup hands together.

That makes a flower;

Watch it bloom for you!
Open cupped hands gradually.

Flower Play

If I were a little flower
Stoop down close to the floor and pretend to cover head.

Sleeping underneath the ground,

I'd raise my head and grow and grow,
Slowly raise up from floor.

And stretch my arms and grow and grow,
Raise arms to the sky.

And nod my head and say:
Nod and smile at one another.

"I'm glad to see you all today."

Follow Me!

by Chuck Schacht, Romeo, MI

First hop forward 1, 2, 3.

Then hop backward just like me.

Hop on two feet, hop on one.

Hopping's such a lot of fun.
Do appropriate actions

Four Little Drums

Permission from "Storytime Treasures,"
1-888-38-STORY

The first little drum
Hold up one finger.

Goes pitty-pat.
Clap hands very softly.

It has a quiet beat.

The second drum
Hold up two fingers.

Goes tap-tap-tap
Clap hands a little louder.

To keep the rhythm neat.

The third drum
Hold up three fingers.

Is a bigger one.
Clap hands louder than before.

Bang-bang-bang it plays.

The fourth drum is the biggest yet.
Hold up four fingers.

Boom boom-boom it says.
Clap hands very loud.

And all four drums together now:
Hold up four fingers.

Bang-Bang-Bang, Pitty-Pat
Clap loudly, then softly.

Boom-Boom-Boom, Tap tap, tap
Clap loudly, then softly.

Go marching through the town.
March in place.

Friends

I say, "Hello," to friends at Storyhour.
*Nod head. Point around circle to
Storyhour friends.*

I'm happy as can be.
They are my special Storyhour friends.
I like them all, you see.

Fun At the Playground

Climb the ladder, and down we slide;
Motion of sliding.

Then on the teeter-totter we ride.
Motion of hands going up and down.

Swinging, swinging, way up high,
Swing arms back and forth.

Stretching, stretching to touch the sky.
Stretch arms as high as possible.

Around we go on the merry-go-round,
Stand and turn in a circle.

Having fun at our playground.

Fun With Hands

Roll, roll, roll your hands
As slowly as can be;
Roll, roll, roll your hands;
Do it now with me.
Roll, roll, roll your hands
As fast, as fast can be;
Roll, roll, roll your hands;
Do it now with me.

*Continue by substituting other
actions—clap, clap, clap your hands;
shake, shake shake your hands; stamp,
stamp, stamp your feet.*

Fuzzy Wuzzy Caterpillar

Fuzzy wuzzy caterpillar
Into a corner will creep.
Make fingers creep.

He'll spin himself a blanket,
And then go fast asleep.
Rest head on hands. Close eyes.

Fuzzy wuzzy caterpillar
Wakes up by and by
Children awaken.

To find he has wings of beauty
Changed to a butterfly.

Funny Little Man

There was a funny little man
Hold up thumb of right hand.

In a funny little house!
Place thumb inside fist of right hand.

And right across the way
Repeat with left hand.

There was another funny man

In a funny little house,

And they played hide and seek all day.

The one little man
Slip thumb between first and second fingers.

Through his window would peep,

And seeing no one, would softly creep

Out of his door,
Slip thumb out of fist.

Out of his door.
With thumb extended move hand forward.

He'd look up

And down
Move thumb back.

And high
Move thumb up.

And low
Move thumb down.

And back into the house would go.
Slip thumb back into fist.

Now the other little man
Repeat the same motions with the other hand for this verse.

Through his window would peep,

And seeing no one, would softly creep

Out of his door.

He'd look up and down,

And high

And low

And back into the house would go.

But one day these funny little men

Forgot to peep,

And out of their doors
Repeat actions.

Did softly creep.

They looked up and down,

And high, and low,

And seeing each other — they laughed —

Ha, Ha, Ho, Ho,
Wiggle thumbs at each other.

And back into their houses did go.

G

Galloping

I like to ride
> *Close fists, thumbs upward. Make large semi-circles with both hands.*

On a gallopy horse.

Gillopy, gallopy,

Trot — trot — trot.
> *Make up and down motions with hands.*

Over the hilltop,

Down through the land,

Leaping the fence
> *Large motion of jumping fence.*

To the barnyard lot.

Oh, it's rillicking — rollicking

Fun — is it not

To ride gillipy, gallopy
> *Galloping motion with hands.*

Trot — trot — trot.
> *Short up and down motion.*

To ride gillipy, gallopy

Trot — trot — trot.

Gently Falling Leaves

Little leaves fall gently down,
> *Raise hands and lower them, fluttering fingers like falling leaves.*

Red and yellow, orange and brown.

Whirling, whirling round and round,
> *Whirl hands as they flutter.*

Quietly without a sound,

Falling softly to the ground,
> *Lower bodies gradually to floor.*

Down — and down — and down — and down.

Going To Bed

This little boy is just going to bed;
Down on the pillow he lays his head.
He wraps himself in the covers tight,
And this is the way he sleeps all night.
Morning comes, he opens his eyes.
Off with a toss the covers fly.
Soon he is up and dressed and away,
Ready for fun and play all day.

Use forefinger for boy. Lay finger crosswise on other hand using thumb for pillow. Use fingers for cover.

Good Bye

Raise your hand
And give a sigh.
It's the end of Storyhour.
Good bye!
Wave.

Good Day Everybody

Good day, everybody!
Nod heads to each other.

Good day, everybody!
Good day! Good day! Good day!
Smile everybody!
Smile broadly.

Smile everybody!
Let's chase the blues away.
Shake hands everybody!
Shake hands with each other.

Shake hands everybody!
Let's make new friends today.

Good Morning

Good morning, merry sunshine.
How are you today?
We've come to our own storyhour
To laugh and sing and play.

Let your hands go loudly clap, clap,
    clap.
Let your fingers briskly snap, snap,
    snap,
And fold your arms and close your
    eyes,
And quiet be.

Roll your hands so swiftly wide awake.
Let your fingers briskly shake, shake,
    shake.
And fold your arms and close your
    eyes,
And quiet be.

Suit actions to words.

Good Things to Eat

Will you have a cookie,
Form circle with thumb and forefinger.

Or a piece of pie,
Form triangle.

Or a striped candy stick?
Hold one finger up straight.

Well, so will I.
Open mouth as though taking a bite.

48

Grandma's Spectacles

These are Grandma's spectacles.
> *Bring index finger and thumb together
> and place against face as if wearing
> glasses.*

This is Grandma's hat.
> *Bring fingers together in a peak over
> head.*

This is the way she folds her hands,
> *Clasp hands together.*

And lays them in her lap.
> *Lay hands in lap.*

Gray Squirrel

Gray squirrel, gray squirrel,
Swish your bushy tail.
Gray squirrel, gray squirrel,
Swish your bushy tail.
Wrinkle up your little nose,
Hold a nut between your toes.
Gray squirrel, gray squirrel,
Swish your bushy tail.

> *Suit actions to words.*

Growing

When I was one, I was so small,
I could not speak a word at all.
When I was two, I learned to talk;
I learned to sing;
I learned to walk.
When I was three, I grew and grew.
Now I am four, and so are you.

> *Suit actions to words.*

Growth

A little garden seed
> *Left hand closed.*

Is lying in its bed.

A warm spring sun
> *Form circle above head with fingers of
> right hand.*

Is shining overhead.

Down came the raindrops
> *Right hand descends with fingers
> moving to and fro.*

Dancing to and fro —

The little seed awakens
> *Forefinger extends from hand and rises
> upward.*

And starts to grow.

H

Halloween

A witch once went for a ride on her
broom
Raise thumb of right hand.

Up through the frosty sky.

She zoomed and zoomed, and she
dipped and zipped,
Make dipping motion with right hand.

And she winked at the moon as she
passed by,
Wink.

At the moon in the frosty sky.

She wore a hat that was pointed tall,
*Make a pointed hat with two
forefingers.*

And a cape that was flowing wide,
Make rippling motion with fingers.

And a fierce black cat with a stand up
tail
Point forefinger up.

Rode merrily by her side,

Rode merrily by her side.

Halloween Characters

Here's a witch with a tall, tall hat;
Hands form a peak over head.

Two green eyes on a black, black cat.
Fingers and thumbs encircle eyes.

Jack-o'-lanterns in a row,
*Hands form balls and move toward
right.*

Funny clowns are laughing, "Ho, ho,
ho!"
Palms on tummy and laugh.

Bunny's ears flopping up and down;
Thumbs at temples, fingers wiggling.

Fairy queen wears a fairy crown.
Thumbs and index fingers make circle.

Gypsy plays a tambourine;
Right fist hits left open palm.

Cowboy twirls a rope. It's Halloween!
*Right hand twirls in a horizontal circle.
Clap on each syllable of Halloween.*

Halloween is Here

When goblins prowl,
Make fingers walk.

And hoot owls howl,
*Make goggles with hands and place
around eyes.*

"Whoooo! Whoooo!"
Cup hands around mouth.

When witches fly,
Flutter hands in air.

And pale ghosts sigh,
Raise and lower hands slowly.

"OOOO! OOOO!"

Boys and girls, don't shake with fear,

It just means Halloween is here!

Hammer and Saw

"Pound, pound, pound,"
Says the little hammer.
Pound fists together.

"Pound, pound, pound;
Pound the nails in tight."
Continue pounding.

"Saw, saw, saw,"
Saw right hand over left arm.

Says the little saw.

"Saw, saw, saw;
Saw the board just right."

Head, Shoulders, Knees and Toes

(Sing to tune of "London Bridges."

Head and shoulders, knees and toes,
Knees and toes, knees and toes.
Head and shoulders, knees and toes,
Eyes, ears, mouth, and nose.

*Point to the various parts of the body
while singing song. Then begin
eliminating words and point only
starting with Head, etc.*

Helping Bobby

Here are Bobby's new white shoes,
Here is Bobby's truck.
Here are Bobby's blocks and books,
Here is Bobby's duck.
Let's help Bobby pick up his toys
And put them on the shelf.
So next time Bobby wants them,
He can find them by himself.

Suit actions to words.

Hello Everybody

Hello everybody, and how are you?
How are you, how are you?
Hello everybody and how are you?
How are you today?

If you're wearing red, you can stand
   up,
You can stand up, you can stand up.
If you're wearing red, you can stand
   up,
You can stand up today.

Hello everybody, now stand up quick,
Stand up quick, stand up quick.
Hello everybody, now stand up quick,
Stand up quick today.

Hello everybody, now jump up and
   down
Jump up and down, jump up and
   down.
Hello everybody, now jump up and
   down,
Jump up and down today.

Hello everybody, now you can sit
   down,
You can sit down, you can sit down.
Hello everybody, now you can sit
   down,
You can sit down today.

Suit action to words.

Helping Mommy Drive

Open the car door,
Climb inside.
I get to help my mommy drive!
Fasten the seat belt,
Shut the door,
Start the motor,
Hear it roar?
Brrr! Brrr! Brrr!
Turn the corner,
Step on the gas,
If the road's clear
We may pass.

Suit actions to words.

Helping Mother

I help my mother.
I sweep the floor.
   Pretend to sweep.
I dust the table.
   Circular motion with one hand.
I run to the store.
   Make fingers run.
I help her beat the eggs.
   Make beating motion.
And sift flour for cake.
   Shake one hand back and forth.
Then I help her eat
   Pretend to eat.
All the good things she makes.

Helping's Fun

When I come in from outdoor play
> *Pretend to open door.*

I take my boots off right away.
> *Remove boots.*

I set them by the door just so.
> *Place them by door.*

Then off my cap and mittens go.
> *Remove cap and mittens.*

Zip down my coat and snowpants too,
> *Remove coat and snowpants.*

And hang them up when I am
through.
> *Hang them up.*

I'm a helper, don't you see?
> *Point to self.*

Helping's fun, as fun can be.
> *Clap hands.*

Here Is a Turkey

Here is a turkey with his tail spread
wide.
> *Spread right fingers.*

He sees the farmer coming so he's
trying to hide.
> *Move left index finger toward right
> hand.*

He runs across the barnyard, wobble,
wobble, wobble,
> *Move right hand from side to side.*

Talking turkey talk, gobble, gobble,
gobble.
> *Open and close right hand.*

Here Are My Ears

Here are my ears.

Here is my nose.

Here are my fingers.

Here are my toes.

Here are my eyes,

Both open wide.

Here is my mouth

With white teeth inside.

Here is my tongue

That helps me speak.

Here is my chin,

And here are my cheeks.

Here are my hands

That help me play.

Here are my feet

For walking today.

> *Suit actions to words.*

Here is the Engine

Here is the engine on the track.
> *Hold up fingers in order, starting with
> thumb.*

Here is the coal car, just in back.

Here is the boxcar to carry freight,

Here is the mail car. Don't be late!

Way back here at the end of the train
> *Little finger.*

Rides the caboose through the sun and
rain.

> *Or children could put arms on shoulders
> of the child in front of them to form
> train.*

Here We Go Up

Here we go up, up, up,
Stretch up.

Here we come down, down, down.
Bend down.

Here we go forward,
Step forward.

Here we come backward,
Step backward.

Here we go round, round, round.
Turn around.

Here's a Ball

Here's a ball,
Form circle with thumb and index finger.

And here's a ball.
Use both thumbs and index fingers.

And a great big ball I see.
Form large circle with arms.

Shall we count them?

Are you ready?
Count with index, middle and ring fingers, thumb holding down little finger.

One! Two! Three!

Here's Bunny

Here's bunny
Make fist of right hand.

With nose so funny.
Make right thumb wiggle.

This is his home in the ground.
Make hole with left finger and thumb.

When a noise he hears,
Make ears by putting right little finger and forefinger up.

He perks up his ears,

And jumps into the ground.
Jump right hand into hole in left hand.

Hojas de Té
(Tea Leaves)

Hojas de té,
(Tea leaves,)

Hojas de té.
(Tea leaves,)

Hojas y hojas
(Leaves and leaves)

Y nada de té.
(And no tea.)

Two children face each other, palms meeting. Quickly flip hands so back of hands are meeting. This is done four times.

Las Hojitas
(Little Leaves)

Las hojitas, las hojitas de los árboles se
   caen,
(Little leaves, little leaves from the
   trees they fall.)
> *Wiggle fingers down as leaves fall.*

Viene el viento y las levanta y se
   ponen a bailar.
(Comes the wind and picks them up
   and they begin to dance.)
> *Wiggle fingers up as winds blow. All
> spin around in dance.*

Tra-la-la-la-la-la-la.
(Tra-la-la-la-la-la-la.)

La Hormiguita
(Little Ant)

Andaba una hormiguita
(There was a little ant)

Juntando su leñita.
(Picking up the firewood.)
> *Two fingers walk over clenched hand.*

Cayó una lloviznita
(When it started to rain)
> *Right fingers "rain" down on left hand.*

Y corrió y se metió a su casita.
(He ran to his house.)
> *Two fingers run fast towards the house –
> underarm.*

Honey Bear

A little brown bear went in search of
   some honey.

Isn't it funny—a bear wanting honey?

He sniffed at the breeze,
> *Sniff air with nose.*

And he listened for bees,
> *Cup hand to ear and listen.*

And would you believe,

He even climbed trees?
> *Fingers of one hand climb opposite arm.*

A House

I will make a little house,
> *Hold hands upright with tips of fingers
> touching to form arch.*

Where two playmates come to hide.
> *Slide thumbs under arch.*

When I peep in at the door
> *Bend hands to look through arch.*

Then they quickly run outside.
> *Slide thumbs out quickly.*

Hop, Hop, Hop

Find a foot and hop, hop, hop!
When we're tired we stop, stop, stop.
Turn around, and count to ten,
Find a foot and hop again!

> *Suit action to words.*

A House For Me

The carpenter's hammer

Goes rap, rap, rap;
*Make fist of one hand and pound in
palm of other.*

And her saw goes see, saw, see.
Move arm in sawing motion.

She hammers and hammers

And saws and saws,
Alternate hammer and saw movements.

And builds a house for me.
Make house outline and motion to self.

Houses

This is a nest for Mr. Bluebird.
Cup both hands, palms up.

This is the hive for Mr. Bee.
Both fists together, palm to palm.

This is the hole for Bunny Rabbit,
Make hole, fingertips together.

And this is the house for me.
Fingertips together, make a peak.

I

I Am a Cobbler

I am a cobbler
And this is what I do:

Rap-tap-a-tap

To mend my shoe.
> *Pound one fist into palm of other hand.*

I Am a Top

I am a top all wound up tight,
> *Clasp hands tightly together.*

I whirl and whirl with all my might.
> *Both hands wind around each other.*

And now the whirls are out of me
> *Stop whirling.*

So I will rest as still as can be.
> *Fold hands.*

I Am a Snowman

I am a snowman, cold and white;

I stand so still through all the night.
> *Stand up tall.*

With a carrot nose,
> *Point to nose.*

And head held high,
> *Hold head high.*

And a lump of coal to make each eye.
> *Point to eyes.*

I have a muffler made of red,
> *Pretend to tie muffler around neck.*

And a stovepipe hat upon my head.
> *Place hands on top of head.*

The sun is coming out! Oh, my!
> *Form circle with hands.*

I think that I am going to cry.
> *Start sinking to floor.*

Yesterday, I was so plump and round.
> *Form large circle with arms.*

Now, I'm just a river on the ground.
> *Sink to floor.*

I Clap My Hands

I clap my hands,

I touch my feet,

I jump up from the ground.

I clap my hands,

I touch my feet,

And turn myself around.

I clap my hands,

I touch my feet,

I sit myself right down.

I clap my hands,

I touch my feet,

I do not make a sound.

Suit actions to words.

I Eat My Peas With Honey

I eat my peas with honey.

I've done it all my life.

I know it may seem funny,

But it keeps them on my knife.

Add an accompaniment with body sounds. 3 claps and snap fingers once. 3 pats on thighs, or clap, snap, pat as many times needed for rhythm. The stamping of feet may be included if desired.

For variety, the rhyme may be said silently and only say certain words out loud. For example: "peas", "honey," but continue the body movements.

I Dig, Dig, Dig

I dig, dig, dig,
> *Pretend to dig.*

And I plant some seeds.
> *Stoop down and plant seeds.*

I rake, rake, rake,
> *Pretend to rake.*

And I pull some weeds.
> *Pull up weeds.*

I wait and watch
> *Stoop down and watch ground intently.*

And soon I know
> *Nod head.*

My garden sprouts
> *Raise hands from ground as if sprouting.*

And starts to grow.

I Had a Little Poodle

I had a little poodle
> *Hold up clenched fist for poodle.*

His coat was silver gray.

One day I thought I'd bathe him

To wash the dirt away.

I washed my little poodle.
> *Scrub fist with other hand.*

Then dried him with a towel.
> *Pat fist with other hand as if drying.*

My poodle seemed to like his bath.

He didn't even growl.

I Have a Red Accordian

I have a red accordian
Hold hands about ten inches apart.

With handles at each side.

And when I pull the handles out,
Pull hands further apart.

The bellows stretch so wide.

And when I push the handles in,
Bring hands together rapidly.

The bellows squeeze in tight.

And this is how I learned to make

The music sound just right.
Move hands apart and together rapidly.

I Have Two Eyes

I have two eyes to see with,

I have two feet to run.

I have two hands to wave with,

And nose I have but one.

I have two ears to hear with,

And tongue to say, "Good-day."

And two red cheeks for you to kiss,

And now I'll run away.

Suit actions to words.

I Put My Arms Up High

I put my arms up high,

I put my arms down low,

I put my arms real stiff,

Then I let them go.

First I swing like this,

Then I swing like that,

Then make my arms real round,

Then I make them flat.
Suit actions to words.

I See Three

I see three — one, two, three —
Hold up three fingers, one at a time.

Three little bunnies

Reading the funnies.

I see three — one, two, three —
Bend down three fingers, one at a time.

Three little kittens
Hold up three fingers at the same time.

All wearing mittens.

I see three — one, two, three —
Bend down three fingers, one at a time.

Three little frogs.
Continue actions.

Sitting on logs.

I see three — one, two, three —

Three little bears

Climbing upstairs.

I see three — one, two, three

Three little ducks

Riding on trucks.

I see three — one, two, three.

I Wish I Were a Circus Clown

I wish I were a circus clown,
Point to self.

With smile so wide and eyes so round,
Make wide smile with hands and place around mouth.

With pointed hat and funny nose,
Make a tent of hands and place on head.

And polka dots upon my clothes.
Point to clothes.

To hospitals and homes I'd go,
Where children cried when they felt low,
Rub eyes with clenched fists.

I'd make them dry their salty tears
Dry eyes with hands.

By wiggling my floppy ears.
Place hands on ears and wiggle them.

If

If your fingers wiggle,
Wiggle fingers.

Cross them one by one,
Clasp hands together.

Until they hug each other.
Hold fingers down.

It really is quite fun.

If I Were a Bird

If I were a bird, I'd sing a song,

And fly about the whole day long.
Twine thumbs together and move hands like wings.

And when the night comes, go to rest,

Way up high in my cozy nest.
Cup hands together to form nest.

If You're Happy and You Know It

If you're happy and you know it,
clap your hands.

If you're happy and you know it,
clap your hands.

If you're happy and you know it,

Then your face is 'gonna' show it,

If you're happy and you know it,
clap your hands.

If you're sad and you know it,
wipe your eyes.

If you're sad and you know it,
wipe your eyes.

If you're sad and you know it,

Then your face is 'gonna' show it,

If you're sad and you know it,
wipe your eyes.

If you're mad and you know it,
stamp your feet. etc.

Repeat first verse.

Suit actions to words.

I'm a Little Puppet Clown

I'm a funny little puppet clown.

When my strings move up and down
Bend at knees and go up and down.

First, I'll stand up,

Then I'll fall down.
Fall to floor.

I'm a funny little puppet clown.

I'm a funny little puppet gay.

Move my strings and watch me play.
Repeat above action.

Now I'm stiff,
Stand tall, arms at sides.

Now I'm tall.
Stretch on tip-toes.

Let my strings go,

And I will fall.
Fall to floor.

I'm Bouncing

I'm bouncing, bouncing everywhere.
*Bounce with knees relaxed, drop to floor
on last line.*

I bounce and bounce into the air.

I'm bouncing, bouncing like a ball.

I bounce and bounce, then down I
fall.

I'm Climbing

Climbing, climbing up the ladder.

Sliding, sliding down the slide.

Now I stop with a bump!

On my feet — up I jump!

Running, running, 'round the side,

Then I'll take my turn to slide.

Suit actions to words.

Indians and Trees
by Pam Earhart, Flint, MI

This is a forest of long long ago—

There are the trees standing all in a
row.
Hold up left hand.

Look very closely, what do you see?

Indians peering out—one, two, three.
*Poke three fingers of right hand through
fingers of left hand.*

Now they are hiding. The forest is
still,
Hide right hand.

Now they are hurrying over the hill.
*Make fist of left hand, walk right hand
over it.*

Ever so quietly, now they are nearing

The tepees that stand at the edge of
the clearing.
Make tepee with both hands.

7

Jack Frost

Who comes creeping in the night
Two right fingers creep along left arm.

When the moon is clear and bright?

Who paints tree leaves red and gold
Brushing motion with right hand.

When the autumn days turn cold?

Up the hill and down he goes
Motion of going up hill and down.

In and out the brown corn rows,
Hand in "out and in" motion.

Making music crackling sweet,

With his little frosty feet.

Jack Frost!

Jack Frost

Jack Frost is very small,
Show smallness with thumb and pointer.

I'm sure he is out today.

He nipped my nose
Point to nose.

And pinched my toes
Point to toes.

When I went out to play.

Jack-In-the-Box

Jack-in-the-box all shut up tight,
Children are down on hands and knees with heads buried in hands.

Not a breath of air, not a ray of light.

How tired he must be all down in a heap.

We'll open the lid and up he'll leap
Leader claps hands and children jump up quickly.

Jack-In-the-Box Sits So Still

Jack-in-the-box
Hands closed — thumb inside.

Sits so still.

Won't you come out?

Yes, I will.
Thumb jumps out.

Jack-O-Lantern

I am a pumpkin, big and round.
Use arms to show size of pumpkin.

Once upon a time I grew on the
ground.
Point to the ground.

Now I have a mouth, two eyes, a nose.
Point to each feature on own face.

What are they for, do you suppose?
*Right forefinger to forehead — thinking
gesture.*

When I have a candle inside shining
bright
Hold up right forefinger.

I'll be a jack-o-lantern on Halloween
night.
Thumbs in armpits — bragging gesture.

Johnny's Hammer

Johnny pounds with one hammer,
one hammer, one hammer.

Johnny pounds with one hammer,
all day long.
Pounding motion with one fist.

Johnny pounds with two hammers,...
Pounding motion with two fists.

Johnny pounds with three hammers,...
*Pounding motion with both fists and
one foot.*

Johnny pounds with four hammers,...
*Pounding motion with both fists and
both feet.*

Johnny pounds with five hammers,...
*Pounding motion with both fists, both
feet and nod head for fifth hammer.*

Johnny now is so tired,
so tired, so tired.
Holding hammering position.

Johnny now is so tired
all day long.
Johnny goes to sleep now,
sleep now, sleep now.
Drop head, close eyes.

Johnny goes to sleep now
all night long.

Jump Or Jiggle

Frogs jump. Caterpillars hump.

Worms wiggle. Bugs jiggle.

Rabbits hop. Horses clop.

Snakes slide. Sea-gulls glide.

Mice creep. Deer leap.

Puppies bounce. Kittens pounce.

Lions stalk — but I walk!

Suit actions to words.

Kittens

Five little kittens
Sleeping on a chair.
One rolled off,
Leaving four there.

Four little kittens;
One climbed a tree,
To look in a bird's nest.
Then there were three.

Three little kittens
Wondered what to do;
One saw a mouse,
Then there were two.

Two little kittens
Playing near a wall;
One little kitten
Chased a red ball.

One little kitten
With fur soft as silk;
Left all alone
To drink a dish of milk.

*Hold up five fingers. Bend them down
as verse progresses. Actions may be
added to fit words.*

L

The Ladder

Climb up the ladder.
Fingers climb up opposite arm.

Hang on to the side.
Right hand around left arm.

Sit down at the top.
Clenched right fist rests on left arm.

And down you slide.
Hand slides down arm.

Leaf Buds

Ten little leaf buds
Fingers outstretched for buds.

Growing on a tree,

Curled up as tightly as can be.
Curl fingers into tight fists.

See them keeping snug and warm
Snuggle fists up under chin.

During winter's cold and storm.

Now along comes windy March

With his breath now soft, now harsh.

First he swings them roughly so,
Swing fists rapidly back and forth.

Then more gently to and fro,
Swing them slowly.

'Till the raindrops from the skies
Stretch arms high, bring them down to floor, moving fingers like rain.

Falling pitter-patter wise,

Open wide the leaf buds' eyes.
Wide arms outstretched, open up fists and spread fingers at word "Eyes."

Let's Go On a Bear Hunt

The children repeat each line after leader.

Let's go on a bear hunt.
Tap hands on thighs like walking.

All right.

Let's go.

Oh lookie,

I see a wheat field!

Can't go around it,

Can't go under it.

Let's go through it.

All right.

Let's go.

Swish, swish, swish.
Rub hands together, like swishing through the wheat.

Oh lookie,

I see a tree!

Can't go over it,

Can't go under it.

Let's go up it.

All right.

Let's go.
Pretend to climb a tree. When top is reached, place hand on forehead and look around. Climb down.

Oh lookie,

I see a swamp!

Can't go around it,

Can't go under it.

Let's swim through it.

All right.

Let's go.
Pretend to swim.

Oh lookie,

I see a bridge!

Can't go around it,

Can't go under it.

Let's cross over it.

Let's go.
Make clicking sound with tongue and stamp feet.

Oh lookie,

I see a cave!

Can't go around it,

Can't go under it.

Let's go in it.

All right.

Let's go.
Cup hands and make hollow sound when clapping together.

Golly — it's dark in here.
Say this with suspense in voice.

Better use my flashlight.

Doesn't work.

I think — I see something.

It's big!

It's furry!

It's got a big nose!

I think — it's a bear!

IT IS A BEAR!

LET'S GO!

Repeat everything backwards and fast — Wipe brow — Make a big sigh of relief — "WHEW! WE MADE IT!"

Little Balloon

I had a little balloon
Make circle with hands.

That I hugged tight to me.
Hug self tight.

There was a great big BANG!
Clap hands loudly.

No more balloon, you see.

But if I had this many more,
Hold up five fingers.

I wouldn't hug them tight!
Shake head 'no.'

I'd just hold onto the strings
Grasp strings.

And fly them like a kite.
Raise both arms high.

A Little Boy's Walk

A little boy went walking
*Hold index finger of right hand erect —
fist closed.*

One lovely summer day.

He saw a little rabbit
Hold first two fingers of left hand erect.

That quickly ran away.
Place fingers quickly behind back.

He saw a shining river

Go winding in and out,
*Extend both hands slightly apart, move
them slowly forward weaving from left
to right.*

And little fishes in it

Were swimming all about.
*Place the palm of one hand on back of
the other, wiggle thumbs in swimming
motion.*

The Library

by Laurie Shaffer, O'Fallon, MO

This is the library.
Open arms out wide.

Here is a book.
Hold hands flat, one on top of the other.

Open it up.
Open hands out, palms up.

And take a look.

Little Bunny

There was a little bunny who lived in
the wood,

He wiggled his ears as a good bunny
should.
*Use forefingers on either side of head for
ears. Wiggle.*

He hopped by a squirrel,
*Hold up two fingers and close the others
on one hand and hop them down other
arm.*

He hopped by a tree.
Repeat.

He hopped by a duck,
Repeat.

And he hopped by me.
Hop over the opposite fist.

He stared at the squirrel.
Stare.

He stared at the tree.
Repeat.

He stared at the duck.

But he made faces at me!
Wiggle nose in rabbit fashion.

Little Cradles

In their little cradles, packed in tight,
Cup hands for cradles.

Baby seeds are sleeping out of sight.
Make rocking motions with hands.

Mr. Wind comes blowing with all his might.
Make sweeping motion with hands.

The baby seeds are scattered left and right.
Wave hands to the left and then to the right.

Little Frog

A little frog in a pond am I,
Form frog with fist.

Hippity, hippity, hop.
Move fist up and down in jumping motion.

And I can jump in the air so high,
Make fist jump high into the air.

Hippity, hippity, hop.
Repeat jumping motion.

Little Leaves

The little leaves are falling down,
Hold hands above head, bringing them down in a rolling motion.

Round and round, round and round.

The little leaves are falling down,
Repeat above motion.

Falling to the ground.

Little Hedgehog

Reprinted with permission. COPYCAT Press, Inc., P.O. Box 081546, Racine, WI 53405

I'm a little hedgehog,

With spines oh so prickly.

Others stay away 'cause

I'm not very tickley.
Make a hedgehog by locking hands together, fingers extended up for spines and thumbs extended forward for a head.

Whenever I'm frightened,

I roll up in a ball.

No one seems to bother me,

No one at all.

Little Jenny Wren

As little Jenny Wren

Was sitting by her shed,

She waggled with her tail,
Shake hips.

And nodded with her head.
Nod head.

She waggled with her tail,
Repeat above.

And nodded with her head.

As little Jenny Wren

Was sitting by her shed.

Little Mice

This little mousie peeped within,
This little mousie walked right in!
This little mousie came to play,
This little mousie ran away!
This little mousie cried, "Dear me!"
"Dinner is done, and it's time for tea."

*Using index finger of the right hand,
touch the thumb and each finger of the
left hand.*

A Little Plant

In the heart of a seed,
Buried down so deep,
Make fist.

A little plant
Lay fast asleep.

"Awake," said the sun,
Make large circle with arms.

"Come up through the earth,"

"Awake," said the rain,
Flutter fingertips down.

"We are giving you birth."

The little plant heard
*Open hands, turn up fingers. Raise arms
as plants grow.*

With a happy sigh,
And pointed its petals
Up to the sky.

Little Puppies and Kittens

One little, two little, three little
kittens,
Hold up three fingers of one hand.

Were napping in the sun.
Bend fingers down.

One little, two little, three little
puppies said,
Hold up three fingers of other hand.

"Come, let us all have fun."

Up to the kittens the puppies went
creeping,
Move fingers slowly toward kitten fingers.

As quiet, as quiet could be.

One little, two little, three little kittens

Went scampering up a tree.
Move kitten fingers quickly into the air.

Little Rabbit

See the little rabbit with his big long
ears.
*Make ears by placing index fingers
beside forehead.*

He stays so very still, but I'm sure he
hears.

For I say: "Little Rabbit, stop, stop,
stop."

But away he goes, hop, hop, hop.
*Make hopping motion with hand. If
more activity is desired, allow children
to hop around the room.*

Little Rabbit Foo Foo

Little Rabbit Foo Foo hopping thru
  the forest,

Scooping up field mice, smack 'em on
  the head.

Down came the good fairy, she said,

"Little Rabbit Foo Foo, I'll give you
  three chances,

And if you don't stop that,

I'll turn you into a goose, Phoof!"

Next morning—Little Rabbit Foo Foo
  wakes up and says,

"Oh, what a beautiful morning, I
  think I'll take a walk.

I really shouldn't, I really, really
  shouldn't, but I will."

Little Rabbit Foo Foo hopping thru
  the forest,

Scooping up field mice, smack 'em on
  the head.

Down came the good fairy, she said,

"Little Rabbit Foo Foo, you have two
  more chances.

If you don't stop that,

I'll turn you into a goose, Phoof!"

Next morning—Little Rabbit Foo Foo
  wakes up and says,

"Oh, what a beautiful morning, I
  think I'll take a walk.

I really shouldn't, I really, really
  shouldn't, but I will."

Little Rabbit Foo Foo hopping thru
  the forest,

Scooping up the field mice, smack 'em
  on the head.

Down came the good fairy, she said,

"Little Rabbit Foo Foo, I'll give you
  one more chance

And if you don't stop that,

I'll turn you into a goose, Phoof!"

Next morning—Little Rabbit Foo Foo
  wakes up and says,

"Oh, what a beautiful morning, I
  think I'll take a walk.

I really shouldn't, I really, really
  shouldn't, but I will."

Little Rabbit Foo Foo hopping thru
  the forest,

Scooping up field mice, smack 'em on
  the head.

Down came the good fairy, she said,

"Little Rabbit Foo Foo, I gave you
  three chances

And you didn't stop, NOW YOU
  ARE A GOOSE! PHOOF!"

The moral of the story is "Hare today
  – gone tomorrow."

Suit action to words.

Little Raindrops

This is the sun, high up in the sky.
Form large circle with arms up.

A dark cloud suddenly comes sailing by.
Move hands through the air in a parallel motion.

These are the raindrops,
Bring arms down, flutter fingers.

Pitter, pattering down.

Watering the flowers
Cup hands to form flowers.

Growing on the ground.

A Little Witch

A little witch in a pointed cap,
Make pointed cap with fingertips touching.

On my door went rap, rap, rap.
Rap at door.

When I went to open it,

She was not there;

She was riding on a broomstick,
Sweep arm through the air.

High up in the air.

Little Turtle

There was a little turtle.
Make small circle with thumb and index finger.

He lived in a box.
Cup hands to form box.

He swam in a puddle.
Swimming motions.

He climbed on the rocks.
Climbing motion with hands.

He snapped at a mosquito.
Snap with thumb and forefinger.

He snapped at a flea.
Repeat.

He snapped at a minnow.
Repeat.

He snapped at me.
Turn hand toward self and snap.

He caught the mosquito.
Catching motion with hands.

He caught the flea.
Repeat.

He caught the minnow.
Repeat.

But he didn't catch me.
Point to self and shake head, "No!"

Lonely Kitten

I'm just a lonely little kitten,
> *Make fist of left hand, thumb for head
> and little finger for tail.*

As lonely as can be;

Won't somebody come

And be a friend to me?
> *Right hand moves toward left with
> walking motion of index and middle
> fingers. When they meet, enclose
> fist in right hand.*

Looking Glass

(Tune of "I Went to the Animal
Fair")

I looked in my looking glass.

What kind of face did I see?

I saw a happy face looking at me.

I guess I'm happy today.

> *This can be repeated with sad, angry,
> etc. Allow children to look in the mirror
> individually.*

Mary looked in her looking glass.

What kind of a face did she see?

Mary saw a sad face looking at her.

I guess she's sad today.

Lunchtime

by Tina Birkholz, Elgin, IL

I'll have a yummy bowl of soup

And a sandwich, too.

I'll nibble, nibble, slurp, slurp

And chew, chew, chew.

I'll drink my milk and wipe my face

And put my napkin in my lap.

Then after such a tasty lunch,

I think I'll take a nap.

> *Suit actions to words.*

M

Magic Wand

by Laurie Shaffer, O'Fallon, MO

This is my magic wand.
Hold up index finger.

I wave it all around.
Wave finger around.

I can wave it high,
Wave finger up high.

Or lay it on the ground.
Lay finger on the ground.

I can make it disappear.
Put hand behind back.

I can make it dance.
Dance finger around.

I can make it lay quite still.
Lay hand in lap.

If I get the chance.

Make a Garden

Dig! Dig! Dig! Rake just so.
Plant the seeds, watch them grow.
Chop! Chop! Chop! Pull out weeds.
Warm rain and sun, my garden needs.
Up! Up! Up! Green stems climb.
Open wide, it's blossom time!
Suit actions to words.

Making Cookies

I am making cookie dough;
Round and round the beaters go.
Add some flour from a cup,
Stir and stir the batter up.
Roll them, cut them, nice and neat,
Put them on a cookie sheet.
Bake them, count them, 1, 2, 3.
Serve them to my friends for tea.
Suit actions to words.

Making Faces
by Don K. Savelle, Charleston, SC

Look at me, a smiley face.

Watch as a frown now takes its place.

Dancing eyebrows, up and down;

I make my eyes roll 'round and
   'round.

Like a rabbit, I make my nose wiggle,

Making faces makes me giggle.

Make appropriate expressions with face.

Me

My hands upon my head I place,

On my shoulders, on my face,

On my knees, and at my side,

Then behind me they will hide.

Then I raise them up SO high

Till they almost reach the sky.

Swiftly count them, 1, 2, 3,

And see how quiet they can be.

*Do actions as described, then bring
hands down slowly and place them in
lap.*

Melting Snowman

Make a ball of soft, white snow.

Pat, pat, pat, and watch it grow.

Big round snowballs, one, two, three,

Build a man of snow for me.

Sun comes out to warm the day.

Mr. Snowman melts away!

Suit actions to words.

Mis Manos
(My Hands)

Dos manos tengo para trabajar.
(I have two hands to do my work.)
Show hands, palms up.

Cinco dedos llevan para jugetear.
(Five fingers to play.)
Five fingers standing tall.

Tres dedos fuertes pueden trabajar.
(Three strong fingers to work.)
Hold up index, middle and ring fingers.

Dos son pequeños; pueden ayudar.
(And two little ones to help.)
Hold up thumb and baby finger.

Con mis dos manos me puedo
   defender.
(With my two hands I can take care of
   myself.)
*Sweeping gesture outward to include all
children.*

Y a mis hermanos, todos del taller.
(And all my brothers, let's go to the
   workshop.)

Mitten Weather

Thumb's in the thumb place,

Fingers all together,

This is the song we sing

In mitten weather.
*Make motions of trying to get mitten on
thumb, then push the mitten down on
the fingers.*

Doesn't matter whether

They're made of wool or leather.

Thumb's in the thumb place,

Fingers all together.

This is the song we sing

In mitten weather.

Monkey See — Monkey Do

Oh, when you clap, clap, clap your
hands,

The monkey clap, clap, claps his
hands.
> *Use motions as indicated by words.*

Chorus:

Monkey see, monkey do.

The monkey does the same as you.
> *Motion toward monkey, then toward
> self.*

And when you stamp, stamp, stamp
your feet,

The monkey stamp, stamp, stamps his
feet.
> *Repeat chorus.*

And when you jump, jump, jump up
high,

The monkey jump, jump, jumps up
high.
> *Repeat chorus.*

And when you make a funny face,

The monkey makes a funny face.
> *Repeat chorus.*

And when you turn yourself about,

The monkey turns himself about.
> *Repeat chorus.*

Monkey Song

A little monkey likes to do,
Just the same as you and you.

When you sit up very tall,
Monkey sits up very tall.

When you pretend to throw a ball,
Monkey pretends to throw a ball.

When you try to touch your toes,
Monkey tries to touch his toes.

When you move your little nose,
Monkey moves his little nose.

When you jump up in the air,
Monkey jumps up in the air.

When you sit down in a chair,
Monkey sits down in a chair.
> *Suit actions to words. Many motions
> and variations could be added.*

The Monkeys and the Crocodile

Five little monkeys
> *Hold up five fingers.*

Sitting in a tree,

Teasing Mr. Crocodile,

"You can't catch me!"
> *Thumbs in ears, waving fingers.*

Along came Mr. Crocodile,

With mouth open wide.
> *Make crocodile mouth with arms.*

Umph! One little monkey down
inside.
> *Repeat, using four little monkeys, etc.*

Moon Ride

Do you want to go up with me to the moon?
Point to friend, self, then to sky.

Let's get in our rocket ship and blast off soon!
Pretend to climb in ship. Swish hands quickly.

Faster and faster we reach to the sky.
Jump and reach.

Isn't it fun to be able to fly?

We're on the moon, now all take a look.
Look down.

And gently sit down and I'll show you a book.
Sit down gently.

Mother's Knives and Forks

Here are Mother's knives and forks.
Interlock fingers, palms up.

This is Father's table.
Keep fingers interlocked and turn palms down.

This is sister's looking glass,
Make peak of two forefingers.

And this is baby's cradle.
Add peak of little fingers.

(*Note:* A good follow-up for this verse is "Rock-a-Bye Baby.")

Mr. Carrot

Reprinted with permission. COPYCAT Press Inc., P.O. Box 081546, Racine, WI 53405.

Nutritious Mr. Carrot

Has green, curly hair.
Wiggle fingers over head

His head grows underneath the ground,
Hands form visor over eyes.

His hair up in the air.
Wiggle fingers again.

Early in the morning,

You'll find him in his bed.
Close eyes, lay head on folded hands.

Give his hair a little tug,
Tug gently on hair.

Out comes his sleepy head.
Raise head, yawn.

Mr. Duck and Mr. Turkey

Mr. Duck went out to walk,
Hold up thumb.

One day in pleasant weather.

He met Mr. Turkey on the way
Hold up other thumb.

And there they walked together.
Move thumbs together.

"Gobble, gobble, gobble."
Move thumb back and forth.

"Quack, quack, quack."
Move other thumb back and forth.

"Good-bye, good-bye."
Nod both thumbs.

And then they both walked back.
Move thumbs apart.

Mrs. Kitty

Mrs. Kitty, nice and fat,
*Kitty is the thumb and the four fingers
are kittens.*

With her kittens four,

Went to sleep upon the mat
Fingers relax upon palm of hand.

Beside the kitchen door.

Mrs. Kitty heard a noise,

And up she jumped in glee.
*Thumb is jerked erect and then the four
fingers. Hand creeps rapidly.*

"Kittens, maybe that's a mouse!

Let us go and see."

Creeping, creeping, creeping on,

Silently they stole.

Back the little mouse had gone,
*Left thumb is mouse. It is concealed in
palm of left hand.*

Back into its hole.

Music At Our House

Mother plays the violin,

Father plays the flute,

Little brother plays the horn.

Toot-toot-toot-toot-toot.

*Make appropriate motions for each
instrument. Actions can be varied by
having entire group do all. The girls
play violins, boys the flute. All join in
playing the horn.*

My Bicycle

One wheel, two wheels on the ground;
Revolve hand in forward circle.

My feet make the pedals go round and
round.
Move feet in pedaling motion.

Handle bars help me steer so straight,
Pretend to steer bicycle.

Down the sidewalk, through the gate.

My Body

by Martha Simpson, Stratford, CT

Point to body parts as mentioned.

Here is my head,

My ears, eyes, and nose.

Here is my mouth

And my teeth in two rows.

Here are my hands,

My fingers and palms,

My shoulders and elbows.

They make up my arms.

Here are my legs,

My knees and my feet,

My ankles and toes.

I think they are neat.

This is my neck,

My stomach and rear.

Put them together,

My body is here.

My Eyes

Here are my eyes,
One and two.
I give a wink.
So can you.
When they're open
I see the light.
When they're closed
It's dark like night.

Suit actions to words.

My Eyes Can See

My eyes can see.
My mouth can talk.
My ears can hear.
My feet can walk.
My nose can smell.
My teeth can bite.
My lids can flutter.
My hands can write.
But when the clock,
Its time does show,
I'll take some books
And away I'll go.

Suit actions to words.

My Flower Bed

See the blue and yellow blossoms
In the flower bed.
The daisy spreads its petals wide;
Hold palms upward — fingers open.

The tulip bows its head.
Bend hands at wrist with fingers closed.

My Garden

This is my garden;
Extend one hand forward, palm up.

I'll rake it with care,
Make raking motion on palm with three fingers of other hand.

And then some flower seeds
I'll plant there.
Planting motion.

The sun will shine,
Make circle with hands.

The rain will fall,
Let fingers flutter down to lap.

My garden will blossom
Cup hands together; extend upward slowly.

And grow straight and tall.

My Hands

My hands say thank you
With a clap, clap, clap.
My feet say thank you
With a tap, tap, tap.
Clap! Clap! Clap!
Tap! Tap! Tap!
Turn myself around and bow.
Thank you.

Suit actions to words.

My Horn

Now I will play my little horn.
Make fists and place them end to end.

I put my fingers so.

And then I lift it to my mouth,
Raise fist to mouth.

And blow, and blow, and blow.

My House

I'm going to build a little house
Fingers form roof.

With windows big and bright.
Two index fingers and thumbs.

With chimney tall and curling smoke
Stand with arms up in air.

Drifting out of sight.

In winter when the snowflakes fall,
Hands flutter down.

Or when I hear a storm,
Hand cupped to ear.

I'll go sit in my little house
Sit down.

Where I'll be snug and warm.
Cross arms over chest.

My House and Tom's

This is my house,
*Hold hands upright with tips of fingers
touching to form arch.*

Cozy and neat;

This is Tom's house
Repeat.

Across the street.
Point away from you.

Every day

My door opens wide
Spread fingers apart.

And away I go
Right thumb walks.

To play outside.

Soon Tom's door
Repeat.

Flies open too,

And he comes out
Left thumb walks.

Calling, "How are you?"
Cup hands over mouth.

We talk and play,
Wiggle both thumbs.

And jump and run;
Make thumbs jump.

Our mothers call

And we stop our fun.
Thumbs stop.

Then in we go;
Thumbs walk back in house.

The doors close tight,
Close fists up tight.

But we wave from our windows
Wave.

To say, "Goodnight!"

83

My Igloo

by Pam Earhart, Flint, MI

My igloo is round with a tiny low
door.
*Make circle with hands then hold hand
low to ground.*

It's made of cold ice and snow.
Pretend to shiver

The inside is covered with blankets
and fur,
Spread hands over wide area.

So it's warm when the winter winds
blow.
Hug self to keep warm.

My Turtle

This is my turtle.
Make fist; extend thumb.

He lives in a shell.
Hide thumb in fist.

He likes his home very well.

He pokes his head out when he wants
to eat,
Extend thumb.

And pulls it back when he wants to
sleep.
Hide thumb in fist.

My Wiggles

I wiggle my fingers.
I wiggle my toes.
I wiggle my shoulders.
I wiggle my nose.
Now the wiggles are out of me,
And I'm just as still as I can be.

Suit actions to words.

My Windows

In my house are windows two,
Point to eyes.

Shining clear and bright.

I can drop the curtains down,
Close eyes.

Shutting out the light.

Open, shut them, open, shut them;
Open and close eyes.

Now 'tis dark, no light.

I can see your windows, too,
Point to neighbor.

Letting in the light.

N

Naptime

"Come little children,"
Beckoning motion.

Calls Mother Hen.

"It is time to take

Your nap again."

And under her feathers

The small chicks creep
Fingers of right hand creep into folded left hand.

And she clucks a song

Till they fall asleep.

New Friends

See this finger! It is Sue.

To Storyhour she came.

She looked and looked around the
room.

She didn't know a name.

Four children looked right up and
smiled

And then they waved at Sue!

So she smiled back, and then she
waved

And took a step or two.

Soon she was clapping with them all

And when 'twas time to play,

She said, "I'm glad we're friends

At Storyhour today!"
Suit actions to words.

Night Time

Before I jump into my bed,
Child jumps.

Before I dim the light,
Pretend to turn out light.

I put my shoes together,
Put hands together.

So they can talk at night.

I'm sure they would be lonesome,

If I tossed one here and there,
Toss one hand to right — one to left.

So I put them close together,
Hands back together.

For they're a friendly pair.

Oak Tree

Here is an oak tree, straight and tall
Stand up straight.

And here are its branches wide.
*Put arms up into air, fingers
outstretched.*

Here is a nest of twigs and moss,
Cup hands together.

With three little birds inside.
Hold up three fingers.

Ocean Shell

I found a great big shell one day,
Hold hands cupped.

Upon the ocean floor.

I held it close up to my ear.
Raise hands to ear.

I heard the ocean roar!

I found a tiny shell one day,
One hand cupped.

Upon the ocean sand.

The waves had worn it nice and
smooth.

It felt nice in my hand.
*Pretend to roll shell between palms of
both hands.*

On the Farm

Here is hungry Piggie Snout;
Hold up thumb.

He'd better stop eating,

Or his tail will pop out!

Here is busy Mother Hen;
Hold up pointer finger.

She likes to scratch for her chickens ten.

Here is patient, friendly cow;
Hold up middle finger.

She's eating hay from a big haymow.

Here is Baa-Baa, a woolly sheep;
Hold up ring finger.

Her wool keeps me warm while I'm asleep.

Here is fuzzy, fuzzy cat;
Hold up little finger.

She likes to chase a mouse or rat.
Move fingers to imitate a running cat.

Once I Saw a Bunny

Once I saw a bunny
Extend index and middle finger of one hand upward.

And a green, green cabbage head.

"I think I'll have some cabbage,"
Make fist for cabbage with opposite hand.

The little bunny said.

So he nibbled and he nibbled,
Make bobbing motion with finger and thumb of first hand.

And he perked his ears to say,
Extend index and middle fingers upward.

"Now I think it's time

I should be hopping on my way."
Let hand hop away.

Once I Saw a Little Bird

Once I saw a little bird

Go hop, hop, hop.
Extend left arm and let forefinger and middle finger of right hand make hopping motion to tip of left fingers.

And I cried, "Little Bird,

Will you stop, stop, stop?"

I was going to the window

To say "How-do-you-do,"

But he shook his little tail

And far away he flew.
Wiggle thumb of right hand. Make fluttering motion with right fingers.

Once There Was a Pumpkin

Once there was a pumpkin
Join the fingers of each hand.

And it grew,

And grew,
Slowly separate the hands.

And grew.
Join hands before you, making large pumpkin with arms.

Now it's a jack-o-lantern

And smiles at you,
With a smile, point to various children.

And you,

And you.

One October Night

A witch, she went a-shopping

One October day,

One October day.

She bought some stew,

And a new broom too,

One clear October day.

A witch, she went a-sweeping

One cleaning day,

One cleaning day.

She dusted her house

And chased out a mouse,

One busy cleaning day.

A witch, she set to stirring

At suppertime,

At suppertime.

She sat down to sup

And ate it all up,

At Witch's suppertime.

A witch, she went to dressing

One midnight hour,

One midnight hour.

She straightened her hat,

Then patted her cat,

One late midnight hour.

A witch, she went a-riding

One Halloween night,

One Halloween night.

She took up her broom

And "ALA-KA-ZOOM!"

One moonlit Halloween night.

Suit actions to words.

One, Two, Buckle My Shoe

One, two — buckle my shoe.

Three, four — knock at the door.

Five, six — pick up sticks.

Seven, eight — lay them straight.

Nine, ten — a big, fat hen.

Count on fingers as verse progresses.
Suit actions to words.

One, Two, How Do You Do

1, 2, how do you do?

1, 2, 3, clap with me.

1, 2, 3, 4, jump on the floor.

1, 2, 3, 4, 5, look bright and alive.

1, 2, 3, 4, 5, 6, your shoe to fix.

1, 2, 3, 4, 5, 6, 7, look up to heaven.

1, 2, 3, 4, 5, 6, 7, 8, draw a round
plate.

1, 2, 3, 4, 5, 6, 7, 8, 9, get in line.

Suit actions to words.

One, Two, Three

1, 2, 3, there's a bug on me!
Pretend to brush it off.

Where did he go? I don't know!
Look around.

Open, Shut Them*

Open, shut them,
Open, shut them,
Give a little clap.
Open, shut them,
Open, shut them,
Put them in your lap.

Creep them, creep them,
Right up to your chin.
Open up your little mouth,
But do not put them in.

Open, shut them,
Open, shut them,
To your shoulders fly.
Then like little birdies
Let them flutter to the sky.
Falling, falling almost to the ground,
Quickly pick them up again and turn
Them round and round.
Faster, faster, faster.
Slower, slower, slower.

Repeat first verse.

Suit actions to words.

*See "Abranlas, Ciérrenlas."

Owl and the Brownies

An owl sat alone on the branch of a
tree,
 Fold hands

And he was as quiet as quiet could be.
 Whisper

It was night and his eyes were round.
 *Make circle around eyes like this: with
fingers*

He looked all around; not a thing did
he miss.
 Turn head from side to side.

Some brownies crept up on the branch
of the tree
 Make fingers creep up opposite arm.

And they were as quiet as quiet could
be.
 Whisper.

Said the wise old owl, "To-whooooo,
to-whooo."

Up jumped the brownies and away
they flew.
 Hands move behind back.

The owl sat alone on the branch of a
tree,
 Fold Hands.

And he was as quiet as quiet could be.
 Whisper.

Pancake

Mix a pancake, stir a pancake,
Pop it in a pan.
Fry a pancake, toss a pancake,
Catch it if you can!

Suit actions to words.

Papas y Papas
(Potatoes and Potatoes)

Papas y papas para Papá,
(Potatoes and potatoes for my father.)

Papas y papas para Mamá.
(Potatoes and potatoes for my
    mother.)
Las quemaditas para Papá;
(The burnt ones for father;)

Las calientitas para Mamá.
(The hot ones for my mother.)

Equivalent of "Patty Cake."

Picnic Time
by Diana Carey, "Festivals, Family and
Food," Hawthorn Press, 1982.

Here's a tree in summer.
Hold up a piece of grass with seed head.

Here's a tree in winter.
*Slide fingers up the grass and strip off
seed heads, leaving grass bare. Keep seeds
pinched together in a bunch between
fingers.*

Here's a bunch of flowers.
Display pinched seed heads held tight.

And here's the April showers.
Sprinkle seed heads into open hand.

Picture People

I like to peek inside a book
Where all the picture people look.
I like to peek at them and see
If they are peeking back at me.
Suit actions to words.

Pin-Uno, Pin-Uno
(Pin-One, Pin-One)

Pin-uno, pin-dos, pin-tres,
(Pin-one, pin-two, pin-three,)

Pin-cuatro, pin-cinco, pin-seis,
(Pin-four, pin-five, pin-six,)

Pin-siete, pin-ocho, pin-neuve,
(Pin-seven, pin-eight, pin-nine,)

Pin-diez.
(Pin-ten.)

*Count fingers or count children by
touching heads.*

Pitter Patter

Pitter, patter falls the rain,
Flutter fingers for falling rain.

On the roof and window pane.

Softly, softly it comes down,

Makes a stream that runs around.
*Place hands together and move them
like a winding stream.*

Flowers lift their heads and say,
Cup hands together to form flowers.

"A nice cool drink for us today."

Los Pollitos
(The Little Chicks)

Cinco pollitos tiene mi tía;
(My aunt has five chicks;)
Show five fingers.

Uno se salta, otro le pía,
(One jumps, the other one peeps,)
Lower one; then another finger.

Y otros le cantan la sinfonía.
(And the others sing to her.)
Lower the rest.

Polly's Birthday

Polly had a birthday.

Polly had a cake.
Make a circle with arms.

Polly's mother made it.
Action of stirring.

Polly watched it bake.

Frosting on the top,
Right hand held out, palm down.

Frosting in between;
Left hand moves under right palm.

Oh, it was the nicest cake

That you have ever seen!

Polly had some candles,

1, 2, 3, 4, 5.
Hold up fingers, one at a time.

Who can tell how many years

Polly's been alive?

A Prayer

Now let us clasp our little hands,
And hold our fingers — so.
And all give thanks for a lovely day,
And off to sleep we'll go.

Suit actions to words.

Pretending

I like to pretend that I am a rose
Cup hands.

That grows and grows and grows and
grows.
Open hands gradually.

My hands are a rosebud closed up
tight,
Close hands.

With not a tiny speck of light.

Then slowly the petals open for me,
Let hands open gradually.

And here is a full-blown rose, you see!

Pretending

I'm a bear. Hear me growl!
I'm a lion. Hear me roar!
I'm a dog. Hear me bark!
As I run out the door.

I'm an elephant with a trunk.
I'm a camel with a hump.
I'm a donkey running races.
I'm a monkey. Watch me jump.

Suit actions to words.

Puddle Magic

The trees and sky are overhead
Point upward.

Until the raindrops fall.
Flutter fingers.

The trees and sky are underfoot
Point downward.

And, oh! I feel so tall.
*Stand on tiptoe, stretch upward, look
up.*

So splash along in puddles,
Kicking, splashing motions of feet.

And then just wait and see.
*Fingers lifted in a "wait and see"
motion.*

You'll walk among the treetops, too,
Point to other children.

And feel sky-high, like me.

La Pulga
(The Flea)

Al subir una montaña
(Climbing up a mountain)

Una pulga me picó.
(I was bitten by a flea.)
*Walk right fingers up left arm. Clap
hands as flea bites, "pico."*

La cogí de la nariz
(I grabbed it by the nose)

Y se me escapó.
(And it got away.)
*Pretend to catch flea on arm and throw
hands in air as flea escapes.*

Pulgarcito
(Little Thumb)

Si pregunta alguien,
(If someone asks,)
> *Extend thumb of left hand and wiggle.*

"¿Quién es pulgarcito?"
("Who is this little thumb?")

Digan que de todos
(Tell them that he is)

Es el más chiquito.
(The smallest of all.)

De los cinco dedos
(Of the five fingers)
> *Extend five fingers of left hand.*

Que tengo en mi mano,
(That I have on my hand,)

Este chiquitito
(This little one)
> *Extend thumb of left hand and wiggle.*

Es el pulgarcito.
(Is the little thumb.)

Pumpkin

Cut into a pumpkin;
> *Pretend to cut pumpkin.*

Scoop it with a spoon.
> *Scooping motion.*

Carve a little mouth
> *Use thumbs and pointer fingers to make mouth, tips touching.*

That is shaped like a moon.

Cut two eyes to twinkle,
> *Fingers form two circles for eyes.*

And a big three cornered nose.
> *Point to nose.*

Use for teeth, ten shiny seeds,
> *Point to teeth.*

And place them in a row.
> *Hands up — palms out — fingers straight in a row.*

The Puppy

Call the puppy,
Beckon with hand or finger.

And give him some milk.
Pretend to pour milk into bowl.

Brush his coat
Pretend to brush dog.

Till it shines like silk.

Call the dog
Beckon with hand or finger.

And give him a bone.
Hold two fingers as though holding a bone.

Take him for a walk,
Pretend to hold leash of dog.

Then put him in his home.
Form shape of imaginary dog house.

Puppy Dogs

Five little puppy dogs
In a kennel door,
One didn't like the crowd,
Then there were four.

Four little puppy dogs
Running around the tree,
Mother calls one puppy home,
Then there were three.

Three little puppy dogs
Playing with a shoe,
Foxy ran to chase a cat
Then there were two.

Two little puppy dogs
Having so much fun,
Rover went to find a bone,
Then there was one.

One little puppy dog
Sitting in the sun,
He went in the kennel,
Then there were none.

Hold up five fingers and bend each down as verse progresses.

Q

Quack! Quack! Quack!

Five little ducks that I once knew,
Hold up five fingers.

Big ones, little ones, skinny ones too,

But the one little duck with the
feather on his back,
Hold up one finger.

All he could do was, "Quack, Quack,
Quack."
*Make quacking motions with thumb
and four fingers.*

All he could do was, "Quack, Quack,
Quack."

Down to the river they would go,

Waddling, waddling, to and fro,
Waddling motions.

But the one little duck with the

Feather on his back,

All he could do was, "Quack, Quack,
Quack."

All he could do was, "Quack, Quack,
Quack."

Up from the river they would come.

Ho, Ho, Ho, Ho, Hum, Hum, Hum.

But the one little duck with the

Feather on his back,

All he could do was, "Quack, Quack,
Quack."

All he could do was, "Quack, Quack,
Quack."

Quacking Ducks

Five little ducks went out to play,
Hold up five fingers on one hand.

Over the hills and far away.
Make fingers run away.

Mama Duck said, "Quack, Quack, Quack."
Make quacking motions with thumb and four fingers.

Four little ducks came running back.
Four fingers run back.

Four little ducks went out to play,
Repeat actions with appropriate number of fingers.

Over the hill and far away.

Mama Duck said, "Quack, Quack, Quack."

Three little ducks came running back.

Three little ducks went out to play,
Over the hill and far away.

Mama Duck said, "Quack, Quack, Quack."

Two little ducks came running back.

Two little ducks went out to play,
Over the hill and far away.

Mama Duck said, "Quack, Quack, Quack."

One little duck came running back.

One little duck went out to play,
Over the hill and far away.

Mama Duck said, "Quack, Quack, Quack."

No little ducks came running back.
Shake head, "No."

Quiet Time

I've just come in from playing,
As tired as I can be.
I'll cross my legs
And fold my hands.
I'll close my eyes
So I can't see.

I will not move my body.
I'll be like Raggedy Ann.
My head won't move,
My arms won't move,
I'll just be still,
Because I can.

Suit actions to words.

Quiet Time

Leader: Children, children,
     What are you doing?
Children: Can't you guess?
Leader: Do you have your feet crossed?
Children: Yes, yes, yes.

Repeat verse using different actions.

Do you have your hands folded?
Do you have your backs straight?
Do you have your heads down?
Do you have your eyes closed?
Are you asleep?

While leader has back to children, an assistant can help the children do the various activities.

Rag Doll

I'm a floppy, floppy rag doll,
Allow arms and hands to fall limp.

Dropping in my chair.

My head just rolls
Turn head from side to side.

From side to side,

My arms fall through the air.
Drop arms limply.

The Rain

Pitter-patter, raindrops,

Falling from the sky;
Wiggle fingers to imitate falling rain.

Here is my umbrella

To keep me safe and dry!
Hands over head.

When the rain is over,
Make large circle with arms.

And the sun begins to glow,

Little flowers start to bud,
Cup two hands together.

And grow and grow and grow!
Spread hands apart slowly.

The Rain

Put up your umbrella
> *Forefinger of one hand against palm of other.*

To keep yourself dry.
Put up your umbrella,
There's rain in the sky.
Pitter, patter, pitter, patter,
Softly it falls.
> *Fingers flutter up and down.*

Hurry home quickly,
> *Make fingers run.*

Before Father calls.
> *Cup hands to mouth as though calling.*

Rain

Rain on green grass,
> *Flutter fingers up and down.*

And rain on the tree,
> *Raise both hands to form tree.*

Rain on the roof top,
> *With hands above head, palms down, fingertips touching, make roof.*

But not on me.
> *Point to self.*

Raindrops

I listen to the raindrops fall
On thirsty trees and flowers.
I hear the rain, "pit-pat, pit-pat."
I'm so thankful for the showers.

> *Suit actions to words.*

Rainy Day Fun

Slip on your raincoat,
Pull on galoshes;
Wading in puddles
Make splishes and sploshes!

> *Suit actions to words.*

El Ratoncito
(The Little Mouse)

Por ahí viene un ratoncito
(There goes a little mouse)
Que le cayó un aguacerito,
(Who was caught in the rain.)
Y corriendo, corriendito,
(He ran and ran)
Se metió en un agujerito,
(Into his little hole.)

> *Two fingers run down arm and hide in clenched hand or run up arm to hide in underarm.*

Reach For the Ceiling

Reach for the ceiling,
Touch the floor,
Stand up again,
Let's do some more.
Touch your head,
Then your knee,
Up to your shoulders,
Like this, you see.
Reach for the ceiling,
Touch the floor,
That's all now,
There isn't anymore.

> *Suit actions to words.*

Readiness Game

Make one eye go wink, wink, wink.
   Wink one eye.

Make two eyes go blink, blink, blink.
   Blink both eyes.

Make two fingers stand just so;
   Hold up two fingers.

Then ten fingers in a row.
   Hold up ten fingers.

Front and back your head will rock;
   Rock head back and forth.

Then your fists will knock, knock,
knock.
   Thump fists together.

Stretch and make a yawn so wide.
   Children stretch and yawn.

Drop your arms down to your sides.
   Let arms fall.

Close your eyes and help me say
   Close eyes.

Our very quiet sound today.
Sh — sh — sh — shhhhhhhhhhh!

Ready to Listen

Let your hands go clap, clap, clap.
Let your finger snap, snap, snap.
Let your lips go very round
But do not make a sound.
Fold your hands and close each eye;
Take a breath and softly sigh:
Ah_____

   Suit actions to words.

Relaxing Flowers

Five little flowers,
   Hold up five fingers.

Standing in the sun,

See their heads nodding,
   Make fingers nod.

Bowing, one by one.
   Make fingers bow.

Down, down, down

Falls the gentle rain,
   Raise hands and wiggle fingers for
   falling rain.

And the five little flowers

Lift up their heads again!
   Hold up five fingers.

Riding the Bumps

Let's ride the bumps
   Pretend to ride in a bumpy car.

As we drive in the car.

Now let's stand up
   Stand up.

And touch a star.
   Reach toward the sky.

Let's all be jumping jacks,
   Jump up and down.

And then,

Let's all stand still
   Stand still.

And sit down again.
   Sit down.

Riding the Merry-Go-Round

Ride with me on the merry-go-round,

Around and around and around.
> *Move one hand in circles.*

Up the horses go, up!
> *Raise arms in the air.*

Down the horses go, down!
> *Lower arms.*

You ride a horse that is white.
> *Point to neighbor.*

I ride a horse that is brown.
> *Point to self.*

Up and down on the merry-go-round.
> *Raise and lower arms.*

Our horses go round and round.
> *Move one hand in circles.*

Rima de Chocolate
(The Chocolate Rhyme)

Uno, dos, tres, cho-
(One, two, three cho-)
> *Count 3 fingers of one hand.*

Uno, dos, tres, co—
(One two three, co-)
> *Repeat.*

Uno, dos, tres, la-
(One two three, la-)
> *Again.*

Uno, dos, tres, te-
(One two three, te-)
> *And again.*

Bate, bate, chocolate.
(Stir, stir, chocolate.)
> *Stirring motion.*

Right Hand, Left Hand

Right hand, left hand, put them on
   my head.

Right hand, left hand, put them all to
   bed.

Right hand, left hand, put them on
   my chest.

Right hand, left hand, put them all to
   rest.

> *Suit actions to words.*

Ring Around the Rocket Ship
(Tune of "Ring Around the Rosie".)

Ring around the rocket ship.
> *Join hands in circle and walk to right.*

Try to grab a star.
> *Drop hands and reach up.*

Stardust, stardust,

Fall where you are.
> *Fall to floor.*

A Robin

When a robin cocks his head
  Tilt head to side.

Sideways in a flower bed,

He can hear the tiny sound

Of a worm beneath the ground.
  Make crawling motion.

S

Safety

Red says STOP
Hold right hand in "Stop" gesture.

And green says GO.
Extend right arm with index finger pointed.

Yellow says WAIT,

You'd better go slow!
With index finger extended wave right hand across body from right to left.

When I reach a crossing place
Cross arms at wrists.

To left and right I turn my face.
Turn head to left — then right.

I walk, not run, across the street,
Demonstrate walking or use index and middle fingers to show first walking, then running.

And use my head to guide my feet.
Point to head — then feet.

Said This Little Fairy

Said this little fairy, "I'm tired
as can be."
Point to each finger in turn. Suit rest of actions to words.

Said this little fairy, "My eyes can
hardly see."

Said this little fairy, "I'd like to
go to bed."

Said this little fairy, "I want to
rest my head."

Said this little fairy, "Come, climb
the stairs with me."

One, two, three, four, five;
they tiptoed

Just as still as still could be.

Santa in the Chimney

Here's the chimney,
Make fist with thumb enclosed.

And here's the top,
Cap with other hand.

Take off the cover,
Remove cap.

Out Santa Claus pops.
Pop up thumb.

The Scarecrow

The scarecrow stands,
Child stands.

With hanging hands,
Outstretched arms.

Beside the farmer's stile.

He scares the jay and crow away
Step in place.

With just a painted smile.
Arms outstretched and a happy grin.

See-Saw

See-saw, see-saw,
Hold arms out straight at sides.

Up and down we go;

See-saw, see-saw,
*Move arms up and down. Continue
moving them throughout verse.*

High and then down low.

See-saw, see-saw,

Fun as you can see;

See-saw, see-saw,

Play the game with me.

See-saw, see-saw,

See-saw-see.

Shiny Shoes

First I loosen mud and dirt,
*Hold up one hand for shoe. Brush off
with other.*

My shoes I then rub clean.
Rub shoe with palm of other hand.

For shoes in such a dreadful sight
*Hide shoe behind back for a moment,
then return.*

Never should be seen.

Next I spread the polish on,
*Join thumb and index finger of one
hand to make polish spreader and
pretend to coat shoe.*

And then I let it dry.

I brush, and brush, and brush, and
brush.
Make fist and brush shoe vigorously.

How those shoes shine! Oh, my!
Extend hand and admire.

Sleepy

I'm sleepy, very sleepy.

I want to stretch and yawn.

I'll close my eyes and just pretend

That daylight time has gone.

I'll breathe so softly, be so still,

A little mouse might creep

Across the floor, because he thought

That I was fast asleep.

Suit actions to words.

Sleepy Bear

by Don K. Savelle, Charleston, SC

This is sleepy bear.
Wiggle thumb up, fingers out.

This is his den.
Curl fingers into fist, thumb up.

When winter snows fall

He crawls safely in.
Put thumb in fist.

But when winter is over
Thumb still in fist.

It's springtime and then,

This sleepy bear awakens
Wiggle thumb still in fist.

And crawls out again.
Pull thumb out of fist.

Soft Kitty

Soft kitty, warm kitty,
Make fist of left hand for kitty.

Little ball of fur.
Pet kitty with right hand.

Lazy kitty, pretty kitty,

"Purr, purr, purr."

Los Sonidos de los Animalitos

(Animal Sounds)

Detrás de doña Pata
(Behind Mrs. Duck)
Clap hands together as a duck's bill.

Corren los patitios;
(The little ducklings run;)

Por allí, por allá,
(Here and there, here and there,)

Cuá, cuá, cuá, cuá.
(Quack, quack, quack, quack.)

Detrás de doña Gallina
(Behind Mrs Chicken)
Flap elbows as a hen.

Siguen los pollitos;
(Run the little chicks;)

Por allí, por allá,
(Here and there, here and there,)

Pío, pa, pío, pa.
(Peep, Peep, Peep, Peep.)

Detrás de doña Cabra
(Behind Mrs. Goat)
Index fingers on head for goat's horns.

Van los cabritos;
(Run the little kids;)

Por allí, por allá,
(Here and there, here and there,)

Ba, ba, ba, ba.
(Baa, baa, baa, baa.)

107

The Space Ship

by Chuck Schacht, Romeo, MI

Up in the sky, blinking so bright
Click fingers together up high in the air.

I think I see a space ship's light.

It zooms very fast.
Zoom one hand past eyes.

Now it's hovering near;
Bring hand to rest in front of eyes.

Do you think it's going to land?

I'M GETTING OUT OF HERE!
Quickly put hands behind back.

The Squirrel

Whisky, frisky, hoppity hop,
Bend elbow to make tree, hop one finger up arm.

Up he goes to the tree top!

Whirly, twirly, round and round,
Twirl finger, run down arm.

Down he scampers to the ground.

Furly, curly, what a tail!
Make tail with left hand and arm, stroke with right hand.

Tall as a feather, broad as a sail!

Where's his supper? In the shell.
Cup hands.

Snappity, crackity, out it fell.
Open hands at bottom.

The Squirrel Gathers Nuts

These are the brown leaves,

Fluttering down,
Flutter hands to the ground.

And this is the tall tree,
Hold up right arm.

Bare and brown.

This is the squirrel
Form fist with left hand — thumb up.

With eyes so bright,
Form two circles with thumbs and index fingers.

Hunting for nuts

With all his might.

This is the hole
Form hole with right thumb and index finger.

Where day by day,

Nut after nut

He stores away.
Place nuts in hole with left hand.

When winter comes

With its cold and storm,

He'll sleep curled up,
Circle right hand around left fist.

All snug and warm.

Squirrel's Breakfast

A squirrel from his tree-house
  Close fingers over thumb.

Poked out his head.

"It's high time for my breakfast!"

He gaily said.

So he ran down the tree trunk
  *Fingers of right hand run down left
  arm.*

And pattered around,
  *Fingers of right hand patter round on
  left hand.*

His bushy tail a-trailing,

Nose to the ground.

He looked here, then he looked there,
  Fingers continue pattering.

Through the white snow,

Till he found a nut,
  Fingers scratch at one place.

Hidden deep down below.

And into his cheek
  *With fingers of right hand pretend to
  put in circled fingers of left hand.*

He popped the nut with glee.

Then Mr. Squirrel scampered
  Fingers of right hand climb up left arm.

Back up the tree.

If you look very sharply
  Shade eyes with left hand.

Perhaps you will spy,

Mr. Squirrel at his door
  Repeat motion of first line.

Ever so high.

Squirrels

Five little squirrels sitting in a tree;
  Point to outstretched fingers.

The first little squirrel said,
  "What do I see?"

The second little squirrel said,
  "I see a gun."

The third little squirrel said,
  "Oh let's run."

The fourth little squirrel said,
  "Let's hide in the shade."

The fifth little squirrel said,
  "I'm not afraid."

When BANG went the gun and away
  they did run.
  Clap hands and scatter fingers.

Stand Up Tall

Stand up tall,
  Children stand.

Hands in the air;
  Raise hands.

Now sit down
  Children sit.

In your chair.

Clap your hands.
  Clap three times.

Make a frown.
  Children frown.

Smile and smile,
  Children smile.

And flop like a clown!
  Children relax with arms dangling.

109

The Star

by Cynthia Stilley, Flint, MI

I have two strong hands to help me,
Stretch arms to each side, slightly upraised.

Two strong feet to guide me,
Straddle legs wide.

And wide light all around me.
Circle arms down to floor, then over the head and return to stretch.

What am I? (A STAR)

Stars

At night I see the twinkling stars
Clasping and opening hands.

And a great big smiling moon.
Circle arms overhead.

My Mommie tucks me into bed
Lay finger in cupped hand.

And sings a good-night tune.
Rocking motions with hands.

The Stars

I watch the stars come out at night;
Look upward.

I wonder where they get their light.
Place finger on forehead.

I don't think they'll ever fall,
Shake head "no."

So, I'll reach up and pick them all.
Pretend to pick stars from sky.

Steam Shovel

The steam shovel scoop opens its mouth so wide
Extend left hand in front, palm up, fingers closed. Slowly open fingers.

Then scoops up the dirt and lays it aside.
Lower hand, dig up dirt, move arm to left and dump it out.

Stop Your Motion

Clap your hands
And STOP your motion.

Turn around
And STOP your motion.

Touch your knees
And STOP your motion.

Everybody run, run, run around the mountain.
Run, run, run around the mountain.
Run, run, run around the mountain.
Everybody STOP!

Suit actions to words.
Variations: Skip, hop, tip toe, slide, etc.

The Storm

Clouds are swiftly floating by;
Dark and darker grows the sky.
Pitter-patter sounds the rain,
Splashing on the windowpane.
Wind is blowing, "Oo-oo-oo!"
Rattling doors and windows too.
Tom's umbrella is so small;
It does not keep him dry at all.

Pouring, pouring, hours and hours;
Water for the thirsty flowers.
Waiting children say: "We fear
That the sky will never clear."
"Look! Sunshine! A pleasant day!
Now we can go out to play."

Suit actions to words.

Storyhour Morning

When storyhour morning rolls
  around,
    Form round clock with fingers.

I get up by myself.
    *Hold left arm out straight for clock to sit
    on.*

I do not need to see the clock
That sits upon my shelf.

I stretch and stretch my arms out
  wide,
    Stretch arms.

As if to make them longer.
    Stretch more.

I stretch and stretch and stretch
    Stretch still further.

For that will make me stronger.

I stretch and stretch my arms up high,
    Raise arms upward.

As high as they will go.
    Raise arms higher.

I stretch and stretch and stretch
For that will make me grow.

Storytime

by Don K. Savelle, Charleston, SC

It's storytime, call all your friends.
    Call with your arms.

Let's listen as the fun begins;
    Hands on hips.

Make your arms go
Flap-Flap-Flap
    Flap arms.

Make your toes go
Tap-Tap-Tap
    Tap toes.

Turn around now, 1-2-3
    Turn around.

And now the other way for me.
    Reverse turn.

Clap three times now,
Clap-Clap-Clap.
    Clap hands.

Sit straight and tall,
You all know how.
    Have children sit.

Stretch Up High

Stretch, stretch away up high,
Reach arms upward.

On your tiptoes, reach the sky.
Stand on tiptoes and reach.

See the bluebirds flying high.
Wave hands.

Now bend down and touch your toes.
Bend to touch toes.

Now sway as the North Wind blows.
Move body back and forth.

Waddle as the gander goes!
Walk in waddling motion.

The Sun

Over there the sun gets up,
Extend arm horizontally.

And marches all the day.
Raise arm slowly.

At noon, it stands right overhead;
Point straight up.

At night, it goes away.
Lower arm slowly and drop down.

Suppose

Do you suppose a giant
Reach toward ceiling, stand on tiptoe.

Who is tall — tall — tall,

Could ever be a brownie

Who is small — small — small?
Crouch down on floor.

But the brownie who is tiny

Will try — try — try

To reach up to the giant
Reach toward ceiling.

Who is high — high — high.

Swinging Birds

Two tall telephone poles;
Clinch fists and raise forefingers on each hand.

Between them a wire is strung.
Extend thumbs of both hands and place tips together.

Two little birds hopped on the wire,
Bend the second finger of each hand and place the tip on thumbs.

And swung, and swung, and swung.
With fingers in position, swing hands back and forth.

T

Tan Tan
(Knock Knock)

*Begin by holding hands together –
fingers touching.*

Tan, tan
(Knock Knock)
Tap "baby" fingers together.

¿Quién es?
(Who's there?)
Tap thumbs together.

Yo soy
(I am)
Tap index fingers together.

Manuel
(Manuel.)
Tap "ring" fingers together.

¿Cómo le va, cómo le va?
(How are you? How are you?)
Middle fingers cross each other.

Kiss-Kiss
(Kiss, kiss.)
*Make sound of kiss and tap middle
fingers together.*

Teapot

I'm a little teapot,
*Place right hand on hip, extend left
hand, palm out.*

Short and stout.

Here's my handle,

And here's my spout.

When I get all steamed up.

I just shout:

"Tip me over and pour me out."
Bend to the left.

I can change my handle
*Place left hand on hip and extend right
hand out.*

And my spout.

"Tip me over and pour me out."
Bend to the right.

Teddy Bear

Teddy bear, teddy bear,
Turn around;
Teddy bear, teddy bear,
Touch the ground.
Teddy bear, teddy bear,
Show your shoe;
Teddy bear, teddy bear,
That will do.

Teddy bear, teddy bear,
Go upstairs;
Teddy bear, teddy bear,
Say your prayers.
Teddy bear, teddy bear,
Turn out the light;
Teddy bear, teddy bear,
Say, "Good night!"

> *Standing in place, suit actions to words.*

Teeter-Totter

Up and down, and up and down,
> *Allow children to choose a partner. One child raises up as the other stoops down.*

High up in the sky.
Up and down, and up and down,
On our teeter-totter.

Up and down and up and down,
See what's to be found.
Up and down, and up and down,
Grass and trees and water.

Ten Fluffy Chickens*

Five eggs and five eggs,
That makes ten.
> *Hold up two hands.*

Sitting on top is the Mother Hen.
> *Fold one hand over the other.*

Cackle, cackle, cackle;
> *Clap three times.*

What do I see?
Ten fluffy chickens,
> *Hold up ten fingers.*

As yellow as can be.

> *See "Diez Gallinitas."

Ten Little Candles

Ten little candles on a chocolate cake.
> *Hold up ten fingers.*

"Wh! Wh!" Now there are eight.
> *Blow twice — bend two fingers down.*

Eight little candles on a candlestick.
> *Hold up eight fingers.*

"Wh! Wh!" Now there are six.
> *Blow twice — bend down two fingers.*

Six little candles, and not one more.
> *Six fingers held up.*

"Wh! Wh!" Now there are four.
> *Blow twice — bend down two fingers.*

Four little candles, red, white and
  blue.
> *Four fingers held up.*

"Wh! Wh!" Now there are two.
> *Blow twice — bend two fingers.*

Two little candles standing in the sun.
> *Hold up two thumbs.*

"Wh! Wh!" Now there are none.
> *Close hands into fists.*

Ten Little Finger Soldiers

Ten little finger soldiers standing in a
  row.
  Hold up ten fingers.

Up the hill – down the hill,
  Hands up — hands down.

Marching they will go.

When they're up they're very high;
  Raise hands high.

When they're down – they're low.
  Lower hands.

Ten little finger soldiers
Marching in a row.
  Marching movements of hands.

Ten Little Fingers

I have ten little fingers,
And they all belong to me.
I can make them do things,
Would you like to see?

I can shut them up tight,
Or open them wide.
I can put them together,
Or make them all hide.

I can make them jump high.
I can make them jump low.
I can fold them up quietly,
And hold them just so.

  *Hold up ten fingers. Suit actions to
  words.*

Ten Little Goblins

Ten little goblins dancing in a ring.
  Ten fingers dance.

Ten little goblins, hear them sing,
  Cup hands around ears to listen.

"Ooooooooooooo — Ooooooooooooo!"

Ten little goblins floating about.
  Hands make floating motion.

Ten little goblins — how they can
  shout,
  Hands around mouth.

"Ooooooooooooo — Ooooooooooooo!"
  Make scary sound.

Ten little goblins out on a spree.
  Hands point through air.

Ten little goblins quiet as can be.
  Right finger over lip.

Sh–h–h–h–h–h–h!

Ten Little Monkeys

One little, two little, three little
monkeys,
> *Holding up five fingers.*

Four little, five little, six little
monkeys,
> *Second five.*

Seven little, eight little, nine little
monkeys,

Ten little monkey friends.

LEADER:
"And do you know what they did?
They got in their boats very carefully.
Be very careful you don't tip over."
> *Carefully climb in boats.*

They rowed, and they rowed, and they
rowed to the shore.
> *Rowing motion.*

They rowed, and they rowed, and they
rowed to the shore.

They rowed, and they rowed, and they
rowed to the shore.

Ten little monkey friends.

LEADER:
"It was so hot, and they were tired of
sitting, so they all stood up very carefully."
> *Wiping brow. Balancing motion.*

They all stood up, and the boat tipped
over.
> *Fall to floor.*

They all stood up, and the boat tipped
over.

They all stood up, and the boat tipped
over.

Ten little monkey friends.

LEADER:
"What are they going to do now?"
> *Very excitedly.*

They swam, and they swam, and they
swam to the shore.
> *Swimming motion.*

They swam, and they swam, and they
swam to the shore.

They swam, and they swam, and they
swam to the shore.

Ten little monkey friends.

LEADER:
"Now, what shall they do?"

They were cold and wet, and they ran
home to Mother.
> *Running motion.*

They were cold and wet, and they ran
home to Mother.

They were cold and wet, and they ran
home to Mother.

Ten little monkey friends.

LEADER:
"And what do you suppose she did?"

She fed them and spanked them, and
put them to bed.
> *Feeding motion, spanking motion and
> sleeping motion.*

She fed them and spanked them, and
put them to bed.

She fed them and spanked them, and
put them to bed.

Ten little monkey friends.

Ten Little Ponies

Ten little ponies in a meadow green.
Hold up ten fingers.

Ten little ponies, friskiest ever seen.

They go for a gallop.
Motion of hands galloping.

They go for a trot.
Motion of hands trotting.

They come for a halt in the big feed lot.
Hands are still.

Ten little ponies fat and well fed,

Curl up together in a soft, straw bed.
Fingers closed in hands.

Ten Little Soldiers

Ten little soldiers standing in a row.
Hold both hands up, fingers apart.

When they see the captain,

They bow just so.
Bend fingers at second joint.

They march to the left,
Move them to the left.

And they march to the right,
Move them to the right.

And then they shut their eyes,
Close eyes.

And they sleep all night.
Place head on hands made to form pillow.

This Is My Right Hand

This is my right hand.
I raise it up high.
This is my left hand.
I'll touch the sky.
Right hand, left hand,
Roll them round and round.
Left hand, right hand,
Pound, pound, pound.
Suit actions to words.

This is the Way We Churn the Cream

(Tune of "Here We Go 'Round the Mulberry Bush")

This is the way we churn the cream,
Churn the cream, churn the cream.
This is the way we churn the cream
To make the yellow butter.

This is the way we dip the wick,
Dip the wick, dip the wick.
This is the way we dip the wick
For a nice, big pretty candle.

This is the way we play the fiddle,
Play the fiddle, play the fiddle.
This is the way we play the fiddle,
While dancing merrily.
Suit actions to words.

This Is the White Sheep

This is the white sheep,

And this is the way

The farmer cuts off the wool one day.

The wool was spun into thread so
   fine,

And made into cloth for this coat of
   mine.

*Left hand is the sheep and right hand
the shears. Index and middle fingers
make the blades that open and close.*

This Little Clown

This little clown is fat and gay.
   Hold up thumb.

This little clown does tricks all day.
   Hold up pointer finger.

This little clown is tall and strong.
   Hold up middle finger.

This little clown sings a funny song.
   Hold up ring finger and wiggle it.

This little clown is wee and small,
   Hold up little finger.

But he can do anything at all!

This Little Cow

This little cow eats grass.

This little cow eats hay.

This little cow drinks water.

This little cow runs away.

This little cow does nothin' at all

But lie around all day.

Point to fingers in sequence.

This Little Pig

This little pig went to market.

This little pig stayed home.

This little pig had roast beef.

This little pig had none.

This little pig cried, "Wee, wee, wee,

I can't find my way home."

Point to fingers in sequence.

This Way

This is the way these girls and boys

Can hop and skip and play,
   Wiggle fingers up and down.

But when their mothers call to them

They mind in just this way.
   *Hold fingers upright and move back
   and forth like children walking.*

Three Balls

Here is a big, round, bouncy ball.
Form circle with arms.

I bounce it, 1, 2, 3.
Bouncing motion.

Here is a ball for throwing.
Form circle with thumbs and index fingers.

I can catch it,

Watch and see.
Catching motion.

Here is a ball for rolling.
Cup hands.

Please roll it back to me.
Rolling motion.

Bouncing, throwing, rolling balls;
Repeat actions.

Let's count them: 1, 2, 3.

Three Billy Goats Gruff

by Pam Earhart, Flint, MI

Three little goats went walking
Three fingers held up.

One lovely summer's day.

They crossed a bridge to get some grass
Three fingers walk up arm.

But a troll got in their way.

They tricked the troll and down he fell
Diving motion.

Into the water wet.

Now three little goats are getting fat
Three fingers held up.

And the troll hasn't come back yet.
Shake head.

Three Frogs

Three little frogs,
Hold up three fingers of left hand.

Asleep in the sun.
Fold them over.

We'll creep up and wake them.
Make creeping motion with fingers of right hand.

Then we will run.
Hold up three fingers while right hand runs away.

Three Little Pumpkins

Three little pumpkins, laying very still
Hold up three fingers.

In a pumpkin patch on a hill.

This one said, "I'm very green,
Point to thumb.

But I'll be orange by Halloween."

This one said, "I'm on my way
Point to forefinger.

To be a jack-o-lantern some day."

This one said, "Oh my, oh my,
Point to middle finger.

Today I'll be a pumpkin pie."

Three Little Leopard Frogs

Three little leopard frogs,
Hold up three fingers.

Sitting on a leopard log,

Eating the most delicious bugs.
Pretend to eat bugs.

Yum, yum!
Pat tummy.

One jumped into the pool,
First finger jumps in pool.

Where it was nice and cool.

Then there were two little frogs.

Glub, glub!

Two little leopard frogs,
Repeat actions using two fingers.

Sitting on a leopard log,

Eating the most delicious bugs.

Yum, yum!

One jumped into the pool,

Where it was nice and cool.

Then there was one little frog.

Glub, glub!

One little leopard frog,
Repeat actions using one finger.

Sitting on a leopard log,

Eating the most delicious bugs.

Yum, yum!

He jumped into the pool,

Where it was nice and cool.

Then there were no little frogs.

Glub, glub!

Tightrope Walker

While the band is playing,

Back and forth I go,

High above the people,

Sitting far below.

While the crowd is cheering,

I sway from side to side.

Now my act is over,

Down the pole I slide.
Suit actions to words.

Tired Bunnies

"Come my bunnies, it's time for bed."
Beckoning motion with hand.

That's what Mother Bunny said.
Finger on chin contemplating.

"But first I'll count you just to see

If you have all come back to me.
Hold up each finger as bunnies are counted.

Bunny 1, Bunny 2, Bunny 3, oh dear!

Bunny 4, Bunny 5, yes, you're all here.

You're the sweetest things alive.

My bunnies 1, 2, 3, 4, 5."

Tommy's Pumpkin

It was the biggest pumpkin
Form large circle with arms.

That you have ever seen.

It grew in Tommy's garden

On the night of Halloween.

He took a knife and cut the top,
Point index finger of right hand to
represent knife and pretend to cut.

Then scooped it with a spoon;
Scooping motion.

Made two round eyes,
Make circles with thumbs and index
fingers.

A nose like this,
Use same fingers to form nose.

And a mouth just like a moon.

He put a candle in it,
Hold up index finger.

And quietly as a mouse,

He crept up and placed it

In the window of his house.
Fingers creep to window.

And Tommy's mother cried: "Oh dear,

I fear some brownies must be hiding

Very, very near!"

The Top

Wind the top,
Winding motion.

Wind the top,

Round and round and round.
Spinning motion.

Now it makes a little hop
Hopping motion.

And spins along the ground.
Spinning faster.

Faster, faster, faster,

Whirling, whirling, whirling.

Spinning round and round again,

Twirling, twirling, twirling.

Wobbly, wobbly, wobbly!
Wobbling motion.

It's running down I fear.

Slower, slower, slower.
Spinning slowly.

Now it falls! Oh dear!
Falling to floor.

The Top

I have a top.
> *Hold thumb and index finger of one hand together to make "top."*

It spins and spins.
> *Rotate top in open palm of other hand.*

Mm-mm-mm-mm.
> *Hum.*

It spins around
> *Rotate top in one palm.*

And soon it stops.
> *Let top flop in palm of left hand.*

Mm-mm-mm-mm.
> *Hum.*

Tortillitas de Manteca
(Little Lard Tortillas)

Tortillitas de manteca
(Little lard tortillas)

Para mamá que está contenta.
(For mother who is very happy.)

Tortillitas de salvado
(Little bran tortillas)

Para papá que está enojado.
(For father who is very angry.)

> *Clap hands together as if making tortillas.*

Touch

I'll touch my hair, my lips, my eyes;
I'll sit up straight and then I'll rise.
I'll touch my ears, my nose, my chin,
Then quietly sit down again.

> *Suit actions to words.*

Touch

I love soft things so very much;
Soft things to feel,
Soft things to touch.
A cushioned chair,
A furry muff,
A baby's cheek,
A powder puff,
A bedtime kiss,
A gentle breeze,
My puppy's ear,
I love all these.

> *Suit actions to words, using soft, gentle touches.*

Touch Your Nose

Touch your nose,
Touch your chin,
That's the way this game begins.
Touch your eyes,
Touch your knees,
Now pretend you're going to sneeze.
Touch your hair,
Touch one ear,
Touch your two red lips right here.
Touch your elbows
Where they bend,
That's the way this touch game ends.

> *Suit actions to words.*

The Tree

I am a tall tree.
> *Both hands reach upwards, arms stretching toward the sky.*

I reach toward the sky

Where bright stars twinkle,
> *Look upwards, arms swaying slowly.*

And clouds float by.

My branches toss high
> *Arms wave wildly.*

As the wild winds blow,

And they bend forward,
> *Arms land heavily at sides.*

Laden with snow.

When they sway gently
> *Arms out in front, swaying gently.*

I like it best,

Then I rock birdies to sleep in their nest
> *Continue swaying, form nest with hands. Place head against hands and close eyes.*

In their nest.

Trees

Elm trees stretch and stretch so wide,
> *Extend arms outward at side.*

Their limbs reach out on every side.
> *Stretch.*

Pine trees stretch and stretch so high,
> *Extend arms upward.*

They nearly reach up to the sky.
> *Stretch.*

Willows droop and droop so low,
> *Let arms hang loosely.*

Their branches sweep the ground below.
> *Fingers sweep ground.*

Turkey Gobbler

I met a turkey gobbler

When I went out to play.

"Mr. Turkey Gobbler, How are you today?"

"Gobble, gobble, gobble, that I cannot say,

Don't ask me such a question on

Thanksgiving Day."
> *Suit actions to words or sing to tune, "Brownie Smile."*

Two Eyes To See

Two lips to smile the whole day through;

Two eyes to see nice things to do.

Two hands to put the toys away;

A tongue to speak kind words each day.

Two feet that errands quickly run;

Make happy times for everyone.
> *Suit actions to words.*

Two Little

Two little feet go tap, tap, tap.

Two little hands go clap, clap, clap.

A quiet little leap up from my chair.

Two little arms reach high in the air.

Two little feet go jump, jump, jump.

Two little fists go thump, thump, thump.

One little body goes round, round, round,

And one little child sits quietly down.
> *Suit actions to words.*

Two Little Blackbirds*

Two little blackbirds sitting on a hill;
Two hands closed, thumbs up to resemble birds.

One named Jack, one named Jill.
Slightly raise one hand, then the other.

Fly away, Jack; fly away, Jill.
Right hand is opened, raised above head, same with left.

Come back, Jack; come back, Jill.
Right hand and left back to original position.

*See "Dos Pajaritos."

Two Little Fireflies

by Theresa A. Miller, O'Fallon, MO

Two little fireflies land on my hand.
"Blink" fingers of both hands together.

One named Sally,
"Blink" left hand only.

The other named Sam.
"Blink" right hand only.

Lights on Sally,
Spread left hand open.

Lights on Sam.
Spread right hand open.

Lights off Sally,
Make left hand a fist.

Lights off Sam.
Make right hand a fist.

Two Little Friends

Two little friends are better than one,
Hold up two fingers of right hand — one of left.

And three are better than two;
Three fingers of left hand—two of right.

And four are much better still.
Hold up four fingers of right hand.

Just think!
What four little friends can do.

Two Little Houses

Two little houses closed up tight.
Make two tight fists.

Let's open the windows
Make circles of thumbs and index fingers.

And let in some light.

Ten little finger people tall and straight,
Fingers up straight.

Ready for the bus at half-past eight.
Fingers run to catch bus.

Two Little Mules

This little mule wants corn.
Hold up right hand, palm inward, thumb up.

This little mule wants hay.
Same with left hand — point toward right.

Give them all what they can eat,

And let them munch away.
Work little fingers up and down as if eating.

Two Little Puppets

Two little puppets,
Hold up both hands.

One on each hand.
Each hand bobs.

Isn't she pretty?
Look toward right hand, wave fingers.

Isn't he grand?
Look toward left hand, wave fingers.

Her name is Bella.
Wave fingers of right hand.

His name is Beau.
Wave fingers of left hand.

Hear her say, "Good morning."
Use high squeaky voice. Bend hand in curtsey.

Hear him say, "Hello!"
Use deep voice, bend hand in bow.

Tying My Shoe

I know how to tie my shoe.
I take the loop and poke it through.
It's very hard to make it stay,
Because my thumb gets in the way.

Suit actions to words.

Tying Shoes

Make first tie before beginning.

Bunny Boy! Bunny Boy!
Make two loops with shoe laces.

Around the ear to there.
Loop them around each other.

Go inside the bunny hole
Pull one loop through the hole.

And I'll show you a pair!
Pull tight.

u

Uno, Dos, Tres
(One, Two, Three)

Uno, dos, tres.
(One, two, three.)
Hold up index, middle, ring finger.

Uno, dos, tres.
(One, two, three.)

¿Cuántas personas son?
(How many people are there?)

Uno, dos, tres.
(One, two, three.)

Uno, dos, tres.
(One, two, three.)

Uno, dos, tres.
(One, two, three.)

Mamá y Papá
(Mother and father)

Mamá is index finger, Papá middle.

Y yo somos tres.
(And me are three.)

"me" is ring finger.

Uno más.
(One more.)
Raise baby finger.

Uno más.
(One more.)

¿Cuántas personas
(How many people are there)

Son una más?
(With one more?)

Uno más.
(One more.)

Uno más.
(One more.)

Ése es el niño,
(This is the baby,)
Point to baby finger.

Y con él son cuatro.
(And he makes four)

Use Your Eyes

Use your eyes, use your eyes;

You can look and see.

If you have on brown shoes,

Come and stand by me.

> *Leader calls for various colors of*
> *clothing.*

Use your ears, use your ears;

Listen now and hear!

What kind of a sound

Do you think you hear?

> *Leader makes sound such as clapping,*
> *tapping, etc.*

V

Valentines

Valentines, valentines, red, white and
  blue.
I'll find a nice one and give it to you.

Suit actions to words.

Valentine's Day

Flowers are sweet, this is true,
But for my valentine I'll choose you.
Each child points to another.

Valentine's Day

Five little valentines were having a
  race.
The first little valentine was frilly with
  lace.
The second little valentine had a
  funny face.
The third little valentine said, "I love
  you."
The fourth little valentine said, "I do,
  too."
The fifth little valentine was sly as a
  fox.
He ran the fastest to your valentine
  box.

*Holding up five fingers, suit actions to
words.*

W

Wake Up Little Fingers

Wake up, little fingers, the morning
    has come.
        Open fingers from doubled fist.

Now hold them up, every finger and
    thumb.
        Raise hands.

Come, jump out of bed;

See how tall you can stand.
        Raise hands higher.

My, my, but you are a wide-awake
    band!
        Clap hands.

You have all washed your faces
    Rub palms together.

And you look so neat.
    Fold hands.

Now come to the table and let us all
    eat.
        Eating motions.

Now all of you fingers run out to play
    Wiggle fingers.

And have a good time on this
    beautiful day!

Walking In the Snow

Let's go walking in the snow;
    Walk.

Walking, walking, on tiptoe.
    Tiptoe.

Lift your one foot way up high,
    Hop on one foot.

Then the other to keep it dry.
    Hop on other foot.

All around the yard we skip;
    Skip.

Watch your step, or you might slip.
    Pretend to fall.

We Can Jump

We can jump, jump, jump.
We can hop, hop, hop.
We can clap, clap, clap.
We can stop, stop, stop.
We can shake our heads for 'yes'.
We can shake our heads for 'no'.
We can bend our knees a little bit,
And sit down slow.

Suit actions to words.

What Am I Baking?

Sift the flour and break an egg.
Add some salt and a bit of nutmeg.
A spoon of butter, a cup of milk.
Stir and beat as fine as silk.
Want to know what I'm going to
    bake?
Sh — sh, it's a secret!
A birthday cake!

Suit actions to words.

What Am I?

A face so round,
    Hands in circle.

And eyes so bright.
    Touch eyes.

A nose that glows.
    Touch nose.

My, what a sight!
A fiery mouth,
    Touch mouth.

With jolly grin.
    Grin.

No arms, no legs,
    Shake arms, legs.

Just head to chin.
    One hand on head and other on chin.

Answer: Jack-o-Lantern.

What Color Are You Wearing?

Leader: Red, red, red, red,
    Who is wearing red today?
    Red, red, red, red,
    Who is wearing red?

All children with red showing:
    I am wearing red today.
    Look at me and you will say,
    "Red, red, red, red,
    I am wearing red."

*Suit actions to words and repeat until
most of the common colors are used.*

Wheels On the Bus

The wheels on the bus go round and
  round,
Round and round, round and round.
The wheels on the bus, go round and
  round,
All through the town.

The people on the bus go up and
  down,
Up and down, up and down.
The people on the bus go up and
  down,
All through the town.

The money on the bus goes clink,
  clank, clunk,
Clink, clank, clunk, clink, clank,
  clunk.
The money on the bus goes clink,
  clank, clunk,
All through the town.

The driver on the bus says, "Move on
  back," etc.

The children on the bus say, "Yak,
  yak, yak," etc.

The mothers on the bus say, "Sh, sh,
  shh," etc.

The wipers on the bus go swish, swish,
  swish, etc.

The horn on the bus goes honk, honk,
  honk, etc.

The wheels on the bus go round and
  round,

Round and round, round and round.
The wheels on the bus, go round and
  round,
All through the town.
  Suit actions to words.

When Cold Winds Blow

When cold winds blow,
  Blow.

And bring us snow,
  Flutter fingers.

At night what I like most
  Point to self.

Is to climb in bed
  Pretend to climb in bed.

And hide my head
  Hands over eyes.

And sleep as warm as toast.
  Place head on hands.

"Shhhhhhh — good night!"

When I Go To Storyhour

When the sun lights up the sky
I sit right up and rub my eyes.
I dress myself with greatest care.
I brush my teeth and comb my hair.
Then off to Storyhour I go,
To hear the stories that I love so.
  Suit actions to words.

When the Leaves Are on the Ground

When the leaves are on the ground,
Point to floor.

Instead of on the trees,
Hands clasped over head.

I like to make a pile of them

Way up to my knees.
Hands on knees.

I like to run and jump in them
Jump once.

And kick them all around.
Kicking motion with foot.

I like the prickly feel of them

And the crickly, crackly, sound.
Click fingernails.

Where Are the Baby Mice?

Where are the baby mice?
Make fist and place behind back.

"Squeak, squeak, squeak!"

I cannot see them,

Peek, peek, peek.

Here they come out of their hole
in the wall.
Show fist and extend it.

One, two, three, four, five
Show one finger at a time.

And that's all!

Where is Thumbkin

(Sing to tune of "Frere Jacques.")

Where is Thumbkin? Where is
Thumbkin?

"Here I am, here I am."

"How are you today, Sir?"

"Very well and thank you."

Go away, go away.

Where is Pointer? Where is Pointer?

"Here I am, here I am."

"How are you today, Sir?"

"Very well and thank you."

Go away, go away.

Where is Tall Man? Where is Tall
Man?

"Here I am, here I am."

"How are you today, Sir?"

"Very well and thank you."

Go away, go away.

Where is Ring Man? Where is Ring
Man?

"Here I am, here I am."

"How are you today, Sir?"

"Very well and thank you."

Go away, go away.

Where is Small Man? Where is Small
Man?"

"Here I am, here I am."

"How are you today, Sir?"

"Very well and thank you."

Go away, go away.

*Point to each finger as mentioned —
then march finger behind back.*

Who Is It? Mr. Clown!

Who is it that wears a smile,
*Use index fingers to pull corners of
mouth up.*

That seems to stretch a half-a-mile?

Who is it that turns it upside-down,
Pull corners of mouth down.

And makes his smile into a frown?

Who can turn his face around,

Why, who could it be but Mr. Clown?

Who Stole the Cookie?

Leader: Who stole the cookie from the
cookie jar?"

Group: "Mary stole the cookie from
the cookie jar."

Mary: "Not me. Couldn't be."
Shake head and point to self.

Group: "Then who?"

Mary: "John stole the cookie from the
cookie jar."

John: "Not me. Couldn't be."
Shake head and point to self.

Group: "Then who?"
And so forth.

Who's That?

Who's that tapping at my window?

Who's that knocking at my door?

That's Tommy tapping at my window.

That's Sally knocking at my door.

"Come in, come in, wherever have
you been?

Join our happy family."

Suit actions to words.

Wiggle

Wiggle, wiggle, fingers

Right up to the sky.

Wiggle, wiggle fingers,

Wave them all good-bye.

Wiggle, wiggle fingers,

Right into a ball.

Now throw it in your lap

And do not let it fall.

Suit actions to words.

Will's Teddy Bear

an English rhyme told by David Rudd,
Chicago, IL

'Round and 'round the garden
*Draw circle around the baby's out-
stretched palm.*

Goes the Teddy Bear.

One step!
Walk up the arm.

Two step!
Walk further.

Tickle under there.

Tickle the armpit.

The Wind

The wind came out to play one day.

He swept the clouds out of his way.
Make sweeping motion with arms.

He blew the leaves and away they flew.
Make fluttering motions with fingers.

The trees bent low, and their branches did, too.
Lift arms and lower them.

He blew the great big ships at sea
Repeat sweeping motions.

And he blew my kite away from me.

Wind Tricks

The wind is full of tricks today.
Make sweeping motion with one hand for wind.

He blew my daddy's hat away.
Pretend to sweep hat off head.

He chased our paper down the street.
One hand chases other around.

He almost blew us off our feet.
Almost fall.

He makes the trees and bushes dance.
With raised arms, make dancing motions.

Just listen to him howl and prance.
Cup hand to ear.

The Window

See the window I have here,
Use hands to outline window.

So big and high and square;

I can stand in front of it,
Place hands on hips.

And see the things out there.
The childen could tell what they see.

Winds

This little wind blows silver rain.
Hold up five fingers. Starting with thumb, bend them down, one at a time.

This little wind drifts snow.

This little wind sings a whistled tune.

This little wind croons low.

And this little wind rocks baby birds

Tenderly to and fro.
Rock hands.

Winter Weather

Let's put on our mittens
And button up our coat.
Wrap a scarf snugly
Around our throat.
Pull on our boots,
Fasten the straps,
And tie on tightly
Our warm winter caps.
Then open the door . . .
And out we go
Into the soft and feathery snow.
Suit actions to words

Wooden Soldiers

Wooden soldiers, red and blue,
Tramp, tramp, tramp, we march for
  you.
  Children march in place.
Wooden soldiers, here we come,
Boom, boom boom, we beat the
  drum.
  Clap hands for drum beating.

First Lines